'I'll be back to

'Tomorrow?' It wa
dared to hope.

'You sound. . .pleased?'

'What do you think?'

'I think I got it right. And have you had the chance to go and buy that dress as I suggested?'

'Oh, it was a *suggestion*? I took it more as a command!'

'Ah, right. I'm glad you got the message.'

'And I bought something. It's—'

'*Don't* tell me,' Nathan interrupted swiftly, then added mysteriously, 'It might be unlucky. But I'll be back about nine tomorrow night. Be ready then. Timing is all-important. Be ready to be whisked away for a very special occasion.'

Alexandra Scott was born in Scotland and lived there until she met her husband, who was serving in the British Army, and there followed twenty-five years of travel in the Far East and Western Europe. They then settled in North Yorkshire, and, encouraged—forcefully—by her husband, she began writing the first of some fifty romantic novels which were to be published. Her other interests include gardening and embroidery, and she enjoys the company of her family.

Recent titles by the same author:

TOMORROW'S BRIDE

DESERT WEDDING

BY
ALEXANDRA SCOTT

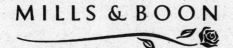

MILLS & BOON

MILLS & BOON and the Rose Device
are trademarks of the publisher.
Harlequin Mills & Boon Limited,
Eton House, 18–24 Paradise Road, Richmond, Surrey TW9 1SR

© Alexandra Scott 1996

ISBN 0 263 79822 4

Set in 11 on 13 pt Linotron Times
02-9611-43931

Typeset in Great Britain by CentraCet, Cambridge
Made and printed in Great Britain

CHAPTER ONE

WHAT relief it was to escape the overwhelming heat. Even among the shady palms about the pool Georgia had felt limp, utterly exhausted after a bare half-hour. But here in the air-conditioned coolness of the club, the day's brilliance filtered through smoky glass, the splash of fountains in her ears—here was blessed relief, soothing, refreshing.

Her eyes were finding it hard to cope with such an abrupt change from brassy glare to shadowy gloom, which probably explained why she didn't at first focus on the figure who appeared from nowhere to greet her.

'Miss Maitland, isn't it? Georgia?' The short man was familiar, at least vaguely, and her frown brought elucidation. 'Grev Canning. We met the other evening at the Kimberleys'.'

'Of course.' She smiled then—that amazing reaction, that slow burnishing of her features, almost an incandescence which illuminated an already striking face. 'I'm sorry; for a moment I couldn't see. I've not really adjusted yet.'

'Well, it *can* take some time. How about a drink to help—something long and cool?' he said persuasively.

'I *had* decided to go back to the flat. I was just on my way to call for a car.'

'Then. . .while you're waiting you might as well have that drink.'

'Oh, go on, then.' She wasn't, after all, in any great hurry. 'Pressed orange with masses of ice.' Sitting down, she let her eyes follow him, watched as he gave his order to the waiter, an immensely tall Arab, his height and slenderness emphasised by brilliant white cotton robes.

The latter had an interesting face—Georgia's artistic senses automatically absorbed such detail—hawkish, a mite condescending, with a red velvet hat at a slightly rakish angle above the grizzled curls and. . . Grev was back beside her on the green leather settee.

'Did you swim?'

'No.' With a shrug she indicated her beach bag. 'Meant to, but it was too much trouble.' And also, though she didn't explain to him, she still had the after-effects of a bug picked up on the journey out.

'It can be a bit of a shock at first,' he acknowledged. 'And you know it's going to be, but nothing quite prepares you for it. Don't worry, though; you'll soon adjust.' Producing a cigarette packet, he offered her one and, when she refused, proceeded to light his own, drawing the smoke deep into his lungs with an air of desperation.

Vaguely she listened while he spoke about his

job—something to do with the harbour board, she gathered—but her attention was detached. She glanced about her with interest, at the groups spaced about the large room, all unknown to her—except there was one... She frowned in concentration. There was a man among the group congregated at the far end, close to the bar.

Her attention was elsewhere when a young woman came thrusting aggressively through the plate-glass doors, not giving the doorman time to hold one open. For a moment or two she glared about her before coming purposefully across to where Georgia was sitting innocently with her companion, her mind wholly taken up with the pleasure of freshly squeezed oranges.

Not until the newcomer reached her table did Georgia notice, and even then that it was more to do with Grev's sudden apprehension, the widened eyes and air of deflation as he put down his glass and got to his feet.

'Greville.' The tone was ripe with all kinds of inflamed suspicion. The woman was red-haired, florid, and dressed most unbecomingly in loud Bermudas and a loose shirt. She grasped Grev firmly and possessively by the arm, at the same time turning the battery of her dislike on Georgia. 'You *are* going to introduce us, I imagine?' And she pulled him down with her onto the sofa.

'Of course I am.' The guilt and helplessness warring in Grev's expression brought a burn of indignation to Georgia's face. Of all things, she hated to feel conspicuous, and the last thing she wanted was to be involved in another marital spat. 'Of course, love. This is Georgia Maitland. You remember, she was at the Kimberleys' the other—'

'And you remember I didn't go to the Kimberleys'. You persuaded me not to, and now—' her voice, already loud enough, rose a few decibels '—now I'm beginning to understand why.'

Heads were starting to turn in their direction. The hum of conversation in the room became subdued, and only pride stopped Georgia from grabbing her bag and making for the exit. Instead, she raised her glass to her mouth and drained it. She gave herself a moment to control her irritation and anger before getting lazily to her feet, to stand looking down at the couple, he sheepish and embarrassed, she challenging and truculent.

'You—' in contrast with the other woman's, Georgia's voice was calm, modulated, melodious even, and, in spite of the surge of indignation revived by the sheer animosity that she was facing, she smiled '—you must be Greville's wife.'

'And you—' the words were thrown coarsely in her direction '—had better remember it.'

Georgia's hands clenched till she could feel her fingernails biting into her palms. Her expression was icily detached, and when she spoke it was with a brittle edginess. 'I think...' She bent to pick her bag up from the floor, taking a first step in distancing herself. 'I think—' again she was aware of being the focus of attention and so forced herself to speak more lightly '—in fact I'm *sure* everyone present will remember, but as for me. . .' She shrugged, but her final cutting remark died on her lips when she saw the expression on Grev's face, and she knew that she couldn't add to his humiliation. The words were choked back and she took another step then turned briefly. 'Oh, and thanks for the drink, Grev. Kind of you to take pity on me.' Then, calm as she could, chin high, Georgia threaded her way through the tables, her entire manner underlining her detachment.

Nevertheless, her hands were shaking slightly, her cheeks were on fire and there was the shaming sting of tears behind her eyes by the time she reached the desk at the end of the room, where she began to ask the steward to arrange a car for her.

'Cancel that.' Again she had failed to notice someone approaching from behind, and the flashing upward look she turned on the man was not meant to disguise her anger at the intrusion. 'I'm going your way, Miss. . .?'

The cool, assessing look, the enquiringly raised dark eyebrow did little to dispel her idea that he knew exactly who she was, and she still had this feeling that she had seen. . .

'Miss Maitland, isn't it?'

'How clever of you!'

Disregarding her simmering anger, he transferred his attention to the steward, who had paused with one hand on the telephone. 'I'm going in Miss Maitland's direction.' And, quite as if she had co-operated in the plan, he put one hand under her elbow to propel her in the direction of the door—a touch which she was so burningly aware of that she shrugged it off the moment they stepped away from the desk.

She spoke through clenched teeth. 'But what makes you think that *Miss Maitland* has any inclination to go in the same direction as you?'

His grin—a momentary flash of white against tanned skin—was disconcerting in its mischievousness. 'I promise you, you have. If only to put one over on your erstwhile adversaries back in there. But, apart from that, we're living in the same block of flats.'

'But that's not to say. . .' Of course. Now she remembered seeing him in the foyer one day.

'Of course it isn't. But, as I say, it will add a dash of spice to the afternoon gossip. It would be a pity to deprive all the ex-pats of a little idle speculation, wouldn't it? Besides, I thought you would want to get out of there as quickly as you could, and that a little moral support might be welcome.'

'I'm not in need of support, especially not the moral kind,' she snapped. 'And if I were—'

'I know,' he sighed. 'I know. If you were I'd be the last man you would—'

'Not exactly,'

Though her manner was irritated, Georgia was struggling with a disconcerting inclination to grin. It was, after all, such a stupid scenario. She was even faintly amused that she was allowing him to control the situation, permitting herself to be guided with quite implacable gentleness out through the smoked glass doors towards the parking area.

'I *was* going to say that if I ever decided I was in need of moral support then a *man* would be the very last person I would approach.'

'Ah, like that, is it?' A flick of his finger brought a long rakish saloon forward.

The parking attendant got out and held open a door for Georgia, who, before she had time to consider, found herself being driven along the palm-shaded drive towards the gates of the club and into the traffic madness of downtown Raqat.

For a time she just sat there quietly fuming, though her brain was busy registering all the sights and sounds which were still comparatively novel. Then familiar landmarks made her realise that they were approaching the block of flats which had for the past two weeks been home.

She glanced at her companion. 'Thank you very

much, Mr. . .?' How strange that until this very
moment she hadn't thought to ask his name.

'Trehearn.' He slid the car into the shaded
parking area, 'Nathan Trehearn.'

'Nathan?' Already she had noticed the accent.
'American?' It was close to being an accusation.

'Guilty as charged.'

'I should think so too.' Self-mockery was the
only defence for her bad manners. She began to
smile. 'I'm sorry, I—'

'I should think so too.' By now he was holding
open her car door, and she was walking with him
towards the foyer of the block of apartments.
'Anyway, only half-guilty, since my mother is
English and I've spent a lot of time there.'

'I *was* being a bit touchy about. . .oh, about that
silly episode back at the club.' The flicker of
amusement had been swiftly replaced by vexa-
tion. Tears were closer to the surface than she
liked. 'I'm sick of married men who. . .'

'Ah.' The range of understanding implied by
that single sound, especially when compounded
by, 'I see,' uttered in such a thoughtful tone, was
impossible.

'No, you don't see.' How could anyone see, or
understand the humiliation which she. . .? 'You
couldn't possibly.' No man could.

They were being swept upwards by the lift.

'No one could,' she said aloud. The movement

stopped. In relief she took a step forward, then said, 'Oh, I thought. . . But this isn't my floor.'

'No, mine.' Again his hand was on her arm—a touch which made her hold her breath, grit her teeth—propelling her across the hallway towards the single door. 'And since we are neighbours I thought it was time I offered you a cup of coffee.'

'No.' She pulled away. 'Really, I'm not in the mood.'

He stood looking down at her—half-amused, half-exasperated, if his expression was anything to go by.

And to underline his intentions he held up his hands. 'No strings.'

Through the open door she glimpsed a dark-skinned, white-clad figure hovering, and for some reason the presence of the servant weakened her resolve. She found, even as she repeated her protestations, that she was being ushered inside, through the cool marble hall into a spacious, shady salon, where she stopped, holding her breath. Wide, fretted arches led onto a veranda where palms, hibiscus and bougainvillea bloomed, filling the air with their fragrance.

A wonderful room. A delight to her artistic senses. Such calm and simplicity was a salve for her ruffled feelings. Subdued gentle colours, sofas covered in natural raw silk, light walls. Two glazed oriental vases—man-size—in dense blue and white were the only touches of colour in the room. At least. . .

Her eye was drawn to an alcove where, carved in polished black stone, was a head. Ancient Egyptian, she would have thought, and catching marvellously well that haughty bearing that so many of the local people seemed to have.

Intrigued and momentarily forgetting her companion, she took a step forward until a movement in the mirror behind the sculpture startled her and she flicked a glance to the reflection of the man behind her. And he, there was little doubt, was intent on her.

He was tall—she tried to be objective—taller than she had at first realised—at least six-two—slim but somehow giving an impression of power, though that could have had something to do with his total confidence. Not *exactly* good-looking— too contained. Except. . . She began at once to shift her ground. Except for the eyes; that luminous grey was unusual, and when fringed with the longest sooty lashes that she had ever seen. . .

Still he was looking at her, one slender eyebrow raised assessingly so she blushed, one hand going up to fiddle with the rope of amber beads that she was wearing, the other to push the fall of thick hair from her forehead. 'What a delightful room.' She gave a tiny self-conscious laugh as she moved away, 'Have you been here long?'

'Eighteen months.' An outstretched hand

encouraged Georgia towards one of the sofas, while he perched on the arm of a chair opposite. 'Now, I did promise you a drink, so what would you like? Coffee? Gin and tonic? Or. . .or what? I think we have quite a range. I usually have a sandwich about now too.'

'Oh. . .oh, I couldn't.'

'Couldn't what?' Not giving her a chance to reply, Nathan looked over her head and spoke to someone out of her sight. She imagined it was the servant who had been hovering since their arrival. A few words were exchanged before he reverted to English. 'It's all organised. Ismail will rustle up some coffee, but, in the meantime—' getting up, he crossed to a cabinet and she heard the clink of glass '—what do you say to a gin and tonic?'

'Fine.' It was her own voice, but shadowy and distant—a reflection, perhaps, of how she was feeling. It was as if her own fairly firm decision-making capacity had been removed. 'But very weak, please.' She must not let him think that she couldn't assert herself.

'Couldn't be weaker.' He handed her a glass, placed a table conveniently close and sat opposite, taking a swallow of his own drink while managing to keep his attention firmly fixed on her face. Leaning forward, he put his own glass onto the tiled table which separated the settees. 'Tell me about yourself.' He leaned back, his long legs stretched sideways, crossed at the ankle.

She determined to be guarded; he struck her as the kind of man to whom it might be too easy to unburden oneself. 'That might take some time and could be extremely boring.'

'Well—' he grinned, teeth gleaming white against tanned skin '—it is Sunday, after all. We have plenty of time—and I promise not to be the least bit bored by what you say. But you don't have to go too far back. What brings you out here to Raqat, for instance? That seems a reasonable place to begin.'

It was a safe enough starting point. 'I'm here for just a short break. You see. . .' Georgia paused to take a sip from her glass—'I'm in fashion design.' And minus a job at the moment, though there was no way that she was prepared to admit as much to this seemingly highly successful man. 'I felt I was running out of steam, was in need of inspiration, and I've always had a hankering to see the desert so. . .'

Leaning forward, she placed the glass with great care on the table. There was something unnerving about such total concentration, however friendly it seemed. 'So here I am.'

'Ah. . .' He paused while Ismail wheeled in a trolley and placed it conveniently for his employer. 'Thanks, Ismail. It all looks very good.'

That was undeniable. The scent of the coffee and the sight of so many tiny savouries reminded Georgia that she had gone without breakfast that morning. She swallowed, accepted the strong fragrant brew when the cup was passed to her and was disinclined to argue when plates of food were offered.

'And the Taylors?'

'What?' Her mouth was filled with a delicious mix of feather-light pastry, cheese and spinach, which had to be swallowed hastily. She dabbed her mouth with the napkin. 'I'm sorry. . .?' She frowned.

'The flat you're in. The one directly under this. It belongs to a young man who teaches locally. He and his wife have gone on leave, I understand.'

'Oh, that. . . Well, that's not a long story. His uncle is a friend of my father's, and it was a long-distance arrangement. I offered to rent the flat for the month that the Taylors are away. So far, it seems to be working out pretty well.'

'But I understood. . .'

'What?'

'No, I've obviously made a mistake. Let me fill up your cup.'

'It's a tiny flat, of course. Just one bedroom— not a bit like this.' Slightly envious of so much space, she looked about her. Then she helped herself to another asparagus roll—wafer-thin bread, buttered and wrapped round stalks of steamed asparagus. 'You must have the entire top floor to yourself. At least, I didn't see another door on the landing.'

'Yes.' Nathan sat back, frowning as he stirred his coffee. 'Yes.' There was an edge of impatience in his voice. 'You're right. I have this vast flat to myself. But tell me how you came to get mixed up with the Cannings.'

'Oh, the Cannings.' She wrinkled her nose. 'Entirely by accident, I assure you. I simply walked through the club to order a car to bring me home and he seemed to appear from nowhere. I couldn't even remember where we had met till he reminded me. And then he persuaded me to have a drink. Oh. . .maybe I didn't need such a lot of persuading. I might even have been glad of some company, I don't know.

'Anyway, no sooner had I put the glass to my lips than his wife appeared and practically accused me of alienating his affections; would you believe it? All in front of a hugely entertained audience. I should think,' she said moodily, 'everyone in Raqat will know about it by now.'

'Well—' he smiled '—you mustn't mind them. Living in such a restricted community means that the most minor drama turns them all into theatre critics. I imagine most of them had to sit on their hands as you delivered your last line.'

'Oh, dear.' There was a rueful side to her laughter. 'I wish I hadn't. But I was, in fact, about to add something worse. I did so want to let her know that poor Grev, married or single, was safe as houses. But before I could I caught sight of his face, saw how crushed, how utterly humiliated he looked and decided to call it a day. Poor man,' she said.

'Yes, poor man. He has the reputation of being totally under her thumb. Whether or not she has any reason to suspect him I don't know, but seeing her in full flow... Could anyone blame him?'

'In fact I found it decidedly unpleasant.' She refused to be persuaded that it had been amusing.

'I'm sure you did. But not, I hope, to the extent that you're wholly disillusioned by men in general, which is what you implied. Surely it wasn't "poor Grev" who had such a profoundly adverse effect?'

'Not him at all,' Georgia agreed sweetly. 'And I don't know that I would agree that the effect was adverse.' And, having no intention of pursuing the conversation as it was currently directed, she got to her feet, placing her crumpled napkin on her plate. 'But now I really must go. Thank you for the help and sustenance; it was exactly what I needed.'

'Oh, must you? What a pity—just when the conversation was set to become interesting...' Nathan was teasing, she knew that, but she was feeling bruised and touchy.

'I'm sorry if I bored you earlier.'

'Did I say that?' He was still amused.

'You implied—'

'Perhaps I should have used the word intriguing. It would have been much more apposite. But your conversation was interesting from the first—so interesting that I want to hear more and wonder if you could be persuaded to come out to dinner with me tonight?'

'Oh, *no*.' She replied almost before he had finished speaking, with a force that caused him to raise an eyebrow. 'I'm sorry.' While determined to remain firm she grew more amenable. 'But thank you for asking me.' There was no way she was ready for another involvement, however innocuous.

'Perhaps some other time.'

If he were disappointed it certainly didn't show—amused rather, she decided with a touch of pique, which might have been why she refused to reply.

But he walked with her to the door, saw her into the lift, stepped in after her and pressed the button.

'Really, there's no need for you to come down with me.' There was momentary panic as Georgia tried to understand his motive.

'I'm not. I've left something in the car, I'm going down to pick it up.' Nathan's tone was so very dry that she had little doubt he was into mind-reading, which must be highly amusing for him.

'Oh. . .' Already the lift was stopping at her

floor, so she could make her escape without further explanation, 'Thank you again.'

But the words died on her lips as she looked across the hallway to the man, youngish and struggling with suitcases, who was trying to gain entry to her flat. 'What on earth. . .?' She strode forward. 'Do you mind telling me exactly what you think—?'

But from just a step behind she heard Nathan Trehearn. 'Hello, Pete.'

'Nat.' The stranger removed an envelope from between his teeth and grinned. 'Good to see you again. How are things?' But as he spoke his eyes moved curiously to Georgia, obviously wondering where she fitted in.

'Much as usual, but. . .' Nathan Trehearn seemed at a loss—curious in a man of such confidence. 'But I don't know that you're expected back so soon.' He sent a glance to Georgia, who was trying to deny the suspicion beginning to nudge at her. 'This. . .is Pete Taylor.'

Still her brain was unwilling to accept the truth. 'You. . .you aren't Lew Taylor's nephew?'

'Yes. But—'

'But you aren't due back.' It was a clear accusation—anything to force aside the reality which she refused to admit. 'Not for at least two more weeks.'

'My goodness!'

He struck his forehead with the heel of his

palm. 'Don't tell me. . .' He took the envelope from the pocket where he had pushed it and glanced at the handwriting. 'For heaven's sake. . . Yes, this is from Lew and. . .it's ten to one they got the dates mixed up and. . .'

Hastily he ripped open the envelope, frowned over the single sheet of paper, then groaned deeply as he stabbed a finger at the date at the top of the page. 'Typical. This must have arrived just after we left for Canada. I'm so sorry.'

Pushing open the door, he gestured for Georgia and Nathan to go ahead, and he followed, dropping his various packages onto the hall floor before going into the main room of the tiny flat. 'I don't know quite what to suggest.' A hand was rasped over a chin much in need of a shave. 'I've been travelling for thirty-six hours and my brain isn't functioning that well. The main problem is that Angie is due in a day or so. We split up so she could have an extra day with an elderly aunt and—'

'Look—' Nathan Trehearn was clearly used to taking control, even, it seemed, where he had no immediate interest '—above all you need to grab some sleep. Why don't you—' he turned to Georgia '—collect your things and take them upstairs while we try to think of a plan? I can ring around one or two people—'

'But. . .' Her whole inclination was to argue, to protest that she had paid four weeks' fairly high rent for the flat, but the sight of Pete trying to keep his eyes open, trying to stifle his yawns made her understand the futility of doing so. 'Well. . . I'm not sure I want to—'

'No one *wants* to.' His tone was impatient, certainly; the glitter in his eyes was saying, *I* don't want to be involved in other people's problems. 'But it is a situation which presents certain difficulties, don't you agree? I doubt if you'd like to spend the night here.' He indicated the four-foot-wide settee. 'And I'm sure Pete fancies it even less after travelling halfway round the world. So, go *on*. . .pack up your things and we'll work something out.'

She glared. Anyone would think that she was the cause of the misunderstanding rather than its victim, but on the other hand. . .there was no way her five-foot-ten frame would fit into that sofa. So she had little choice but to go along with his suggestion. It was becoming a habit—one she didn't like!

'Oh. . .very well.' She knew that she was sounding ungracious, but as she pulled shirts and dresses from hangers, folded them carelessly into cases, she simmered with quiet rage.

Going back and forward to the bathroom to pick up her toiletries, she could catch the murmur of voices, one rather dominant—well, of course— and then, her packing completed, she began to pull the largest case into the hall, only to find that

that was taken out of her hands as well. And a moment later, with the sound of Pete's apologies and the sight of his undisguised relief fresh in her mind, she and Nathan were heading back upstairs.

'Damn. Damn. Damn.' Inside the penthouse, Georgia could control her fury no longer, and didn't even try. 'That's right. Get it off your chest. You've every right to be angry.'

'You surprise me. Downstairs it seemed I was the one without rights. He was the one with all the cards though why should I be surprised?' She was allowing her anger full rein. 'In a country like this only men have rights. Even the car is solely for the benefit of the male!'

'Oh, I don't know.' His mildness was an affront. 'I did bring you home this afternoon.'

'No, you didn't.' She raked a distracted hand through her hair. '*You* came home, I. . .' Her voice wobbled. 'I just. . .'

'Don't get upset.' Frowning, he came a step closer. 'Don't worry. There's no great problem. You can stay here as long as you like.'

'Here?' Her eyes flew wide; she stared up and backed away. 'But. . . I've no intention of staying here. You said you would ring round some friends.'

'You're right. I did have something else in mind, but on reflection. . . There's masses of room; you noticed that for yourself. Why, just behind you is a self-contained suite.'

'No, I don't want to. Besides. . .how can I?' Humiliation tore at her; twice in as many hours this man had seen her humbled. 'I would have been better staying down there.'

'Hardly. As you've already worked out for yourself, four of the lower apartments would fit into this one.'

'I'll try for a hotel; there must be plenty of places.'

'Raqat isn't Riyadh or Amman. There are only a few western-style hotels in the sheikhdom—most of them booked up in advance and very expensive.'

'Then I'll fly home!' An idle threat, for it was the last thing she wanted to do.

'That would be a pity.' He smiled, so persuasively that Georgia was diverted and began to revise her earlier idea that Nathan wasn't particularly good-looking. He had the most entrancing smile! The unusual eyes sparkled mischievously. 'As well as being difficult. Flights are usually booked well in advance too.'

She spoke through gritted teeth. 'I'm beginning to wonder what on earth I'm doing here, and if I'll ever escape!'

'As far as the first goes, you might remember it was a question I asked you earlier and which made you head for the door.'

'Really.' A totally inadequate reply, and, to compensate, her tone was heavy with sarcasm.

'And secondly,' Nathan went on, as if she hadn't interrupted, 'Stay. Then you might find you've no desire to.' Then, taking pity on her puzzled expression, he added, 'To escape.'

'That I very much doubt.'

'Well, in the meantime, why not take up my earlier proposition?'

'Proposition?' Georgia was twitchy, nervous as a faun.

'I suggested we go out to dinner so you could continue your life story. I'm repeating the suggestion.'

Staring up at him suspiciously, she had to subdue an infantile inclination to giggle. 'Do I have a choice?'

'Right now, I'd say not much, but as far as it goes it doesn't seem an unreasonable suggestion. Look.' He took a step past her and opened a door which she could see led into another hallway, and she followed him into a spacious bedroom, infinitely more glamorous than the one she had been using downstairs. 'You can use this—bathroom over there, by the way—for. . .well, as long as you care to stay.'

'As long as that, eh? You sound just like the devil: tempting.'

'No strings.' Again grinning, he opened his hands.

'All right. Thank you.'

'Good.' Then he became businesslike, went out, and returned with her cases, which he slung onto the rack in the hallway. 'If you want any help, ring this—' he indicated a bell pull '—and Enna, Ismail's wife will come. In the meantime I'm sure you'd like some tea. I'll get her to bring some for you.'

'Thank you.' All at once she was exhausted, had lost any inclination to struggle against her immediate fate. Her sole concern now was to lie down on one of the beds and to sleep.

'We'll leave here about nine if that suits you and. . .' his hesitation was momentary '. . .I'll have a proposal to put to you.'

Nathan was gone before the last words registered. Georgia swung round as the door closed quietly, but lacked the energy to pursue him for clarification. Instead, she looked about the room—at the two double beds covered in pale grey brocade, the marble floors, veined in palest pink, with that same colour hinted at in the diaphanous hangings at the windows, and the mirrored cupboards covering one wall and adding to the impression of space. There were touches of pink in the lamps too, and in the chaise longue covered in silk. She sighed, partly in pleasure, then went forward and sank onto the stool in front of the dressing table.

The day had been endless. Given the fact that

she'd woken up still suffering the vague aftermath of that tummy bug—now thankfully gone—followed by the fiasco at the club and then the indignity of losing her accommodation, she would hardly have been surprised to find that she had aged ten years, but, on the contrary, a critical glance in the mirror confirmed that she looked remarkably unchanged.

She laid the back of her hand against her cheek, smoothing the firm skin to which the climate had given a peachy glow. It seemed to enhance her green eyes and bring highlights to the dark blonde hair.

Again she sighed, this time from sheer dejection. To think that she had come all this way to try to get her life back in order and here she was apparently having exchanged one set of problems for another.

Raising her arms, she lifted the amber beads over her head and dropped them onto the dressing table. Another sideways look in the mirror confirmed that her cotton lawn dress still looked fairly fresh, even if it felt a little damp. The softly gathered lines suited her tall, slender figure and. . .yes, she *was* still recognisable as the elegant Miss Georgia, who had been assistant designer to the well-known Jordan Severs. And—the unwelcome thought almost brought tears to her eyes—very nearly his lover.

If it hadn't been for the chance telephone call

which had revealed the presence of his wife and family, she would at this very moment have been sharing a bed with him on some romantic hide-away Caribbean island, and. . .

A tap at the door made her reach for the just-discarded dress and hold it protectively in front of her, then she sighed in relief as she saw the maid skimming across the floor with the tea-tray. She thanked the woman, who returned her smile shyly and left the room while Georgia reached eagerly for the teapot.

Twenty minutes later, freshly showered, she lay drowsing on the oh, so comfortable bed, until a thought flashed disturbingly into her mind—one startling enough to take her into a semi-sitting position, supported on her elbows and staring into the mid-distance. Then, after a moment's frowning contemplation, she subsided, a faint smile on her mouth.

A proposition to put to her. Was that what Nathan Trehearn had said? Or had it been a proposal? Well, he would soon see that she was expert at deflecting propositions; she had weakened only once, and that experience with Jordan had honed her skill to razor sharpness. So, unless his idea had something in it for *her*, he would find that he was wasting his time.

She snuggled down, her cheek burrowing into the cool softness of the pillow, and no longer tried to fight the waves of delicious drowsiness washing

over her. A 'proposal'—*that* had been the word,
but she was fairly certain marriage was the last
thing he had in mind. She smiled to herself at the
very notion. And that was just as well, for she had
no interest in any sort of commitment permanent
or temporary; Jordan had cured her of any inclination in that direction for a very long time.

That said, the two men could hardly be more
different—Jordan, with his shoulder-length mane
of almost white hair, and this other, so very crisp
and clean and conventional. Nathan's very difference implied a certain degree of safety, so long as
the present situation continued.

Yes, that was a reassuring thought. Georgia
wriggled slightly in the supreme comfort of the
large bed. Until now, she had always enjoyed the
company of the slightly Bohemian type of which
Jordan was a striking example. She was certain
that his flamboyant temperament had had a deal
to do with the immediate attraction she had felt.
Much of it, as she had already guessed, was sheer
affectation, but it had without doubt added to the
aura of glamour with which he surrounded
himself.

In fact, now that she was out of it she could
assess things so much more dispassionately. His
habit of surrounding himself with tall, good-looking young women contributed to the public man,
whereas Nat Trehearn. . .it was impossible to

imagine him descending to such theatrical tricks. She smiled to herself at the very idea.

But it was strange—her eyes flicked open for a moment—she didn't even know what he did for a living. Strange, strange and passing strange... Here she was, in this house, alone with the man except for a pair of Arab servants—a man whom she had met just a few hours earlier. And the only thing she knew about him was his name.

Slowly, gently, her eyelids drooped, her breathing lengthened and she slept.

CHAPTER TWO

GETTING ready later in the evening, Georgia abandoned reticence, for some inexplicable reason chose to wear one of her more original outfits—the wide trousers which might, until she moved, have been a skirt.

Sheer silk organza, they drifted about her, giving tantalising glimpses of long, slender legs. Their colour—deep sea-green, a shade or two darker than her eyes—was one that she found irresistible, especially when scattered with cream polka dots. The tunic top, in the same silk but without the spots, had tiny puff sleeves with rich cream embroidery outlining the plain round neck.

It was all perfectly modest and restrained, but at the same time, standing in front of the long mirrors, she felt a qualm as she recognised the extremely potent image that she was seeing. It was as if—and this could not have been further from the truth—she were going out on a proper date, with a man she wanted to *attract*, for heaven's sake.

Perhaps if she had taken less care with her make-up. . .only someone who knew nothing about it would imagine that it was casual and understated—that was exactly where the skill lay. Her eyes were emphasised with grey-green shadow, long, carefully curled lashes gave a romantic, luminous look, blusher merely touched the high cheekbones, and lips were barely brushed with a soft sheen.

But possibly it was hair which made the most positive statement, for, after washing it and treating it to an extravagant amount of conditioner, she had decided, after much trial and error, on a plait, which now hung over one shoulder and for some reason looked devastating. Hard to explain why. Was it the contrast between the sophistication of her outfit and the schoolgirl hairdo which gave it such appeal? Perhaps.

Perfume. Of course. She had always loved it. Turning, she picked up the bottle from the dressing table but, as she pressed the atomiser quite suddenly she panicked. This was all *wrong*; she wasn't going out on a romantic date, and it was certainly the last message she wanted to send out to a man who had simply taken pity on her.

Perhaps the wisest thing would be a quick change into a simple skirt and blouse—but no. . . someone was at the bedroom door. Her heart started to hammer, but it was Enna with the message, 'Master is waiting.'

'Thank you, Enna.' So what if she looked good? she thought. She slipped her feet into high-heeled mules, picked up her handbag and did a final check in the glass. She had always—at least, mostly—dressed to please Georgia Maitland, and this was not the moment to change the habits of a lifetime. She smiled rather grimly at her reflection and went to join 'master' in the hall.

And there was little doubt that Nathan, handsome or not—she still reserved judgement on that—was the kind of man who would attract attention. It had a great deal to do with his height, plus his width of shoulder. Men of his shape—powerful, slim-hipped—always pleased aesthetically, and there were other aspects that she could also approve. He was wearing dark trousers, white shirt, a tie in maroon with blue stripes and, over his shoulder, hooked on one forefinger, a lightweight dark jacket. Impeccable and. . .surprisingly attractive.

But was her appreciation of the more conventional style simply a reflection of her anger with Jordan. . .? A faint whiff of some masculine cologne distracted her and found an echo in his first remark.

'Ah, you smell nice.'

'Thank you.' Not a word about her appearance. Not that she'd looked for any—didn't want it, for heaven's sake.

There was no conversation as they dropped to ground lift in the lift, but she was very aware of him—aware in the curious little prickle at the nape of her neck, in the slightly increased beat of her pulse. And there was little conversation in the car as they negotiated busy streets, then turned into a quieter area, through old narrow lanes which criss-crossed the ancient city, driving at last through an elaborate arched gateway, along a drive and into what appeared to have been the garden of a villa which now was a smart restaurant with tables and chairs set out under a canopy of vines and fragrant climbing plants.

'How wonderful.' She looked round with appreciation as Nathan held open the car door for her to step outside.

· 'I thought you would like it. There's quite a large garden. Let me show you round before we eat.'

Again his hand was on her elbow, guiding her along the path which meandered through a small shrubbery into a formal walled garden with a large fountain spilling water into a lily pond. Here, when she sat on the edge and trailed her fingers in the cool water, a brilliantly coloured fish came up and nibbled her fingers in its search for titbits.

'Ouch.' She smiled. 'I came here to eat, not to be eaten.'

'They always live in hope, but feeding the fish is not encouraged; it shortens their lives if they're overfed. But I can see you're feeling hungry so. . .' They were walking round the side of the large, elegant villa; through open windows they could see diners inside. There was an air of wealth and opulence which Georgia supposed was a reflection of the recently arrived oil riches. 'This is the main restaurant, as you can see, but if you prefer we can eat outside in the garden. . .'

'Oh, outside! Please!' Her appealing upward glance failed to register his changed expression, missed the way his eyes lingered on her animated features as she looked around. 'Please,' she repeated, this time smiling up at him, and was gratified by a slow smile in response.

'Of course.' His hand touched her elbow as they followed the waiter. 'It's what I prefer myself.'

'Mmm. Perfect.' She put her handbag onto the table and took the chair offered by the waiter, while her companion sat opposite. 'How can anyone bear to be inside on a night like this and in such a setting?'

'I prefer it to the more westernised places, though there have been lots of those since the oil came. But here you at least get the impression of reaching out to the old Raqat, brushing against the ancient culture.' Menus appeared and he waited a moment while she opened hers. 'I hope you're hungry. Portions tend to be on the generous side.'

'I'm starving.' She forgot to be inhibited. 'It's the first time since I arrived. I picked up some bug on the flight out and I just haven't felt like eating.' Realising what she was saying, she felt embarrassed, coloured up and flicked a glance at him to see if he had noticed, and of course he had. An amused eyebrow was raised.

'Ah?' A short sound could speak volumes.

'It was nothing much really, but I was afraid to risk anything much beyond an omelette.'

'I'm glad you're past that stage now. Maybe best to avoid anything too spicy, though. Couscous can be very easy to eat and comforting. A Scotsman I know says it has the same beneficial effects as porridge. And some of the lamb dishes are very good.'

'Then I shall trust you to choose for me, Mr...' She paused, feeling foolish that in these informal times she hadn't got round to using his name directly. 'Help!' Best to make a joke of it. 'I don't know what I should call you.'

Because he was busy with the waiter he made no immediate reply, but when they were alone again his eyes sparkled. 'For my part, I've no intention of calling you anything but Georgia. And my friends call me Nat.'

'Nat,' she repeated reflectively. 'I don't think I've ever known a Nat before. Well, thank you for bringing me; it's a magical place.' She sat back in the chair, turning her face up so that she could see through the trellis to the sky. 'Why—why is the sky so different here? Millions of stars on a backdrop of black velvet.'

'That's why you came, isn't it? You were curious about the desert.'

'Yes, of course. At least, one of the reasons. . .' her voice faded.

'And the others?' Nat looked up to nod at the waiter who had filled their glasses, then looked enquiringly at her when the man had withdrawn.

'Don't let us bother about that.' Adopting her most consciously seductive smile, Georgia leaned her elbows on the table and took the glass to her mouth. 'Mmm, delicious. I'm sure it would be much more interesting, even intriguing to know what you're doing here.'

'That—' his eyes were intent on hers as he leaned forward, his manner relaxed and amused '—I contradict completely. But. . . I'm quite happy to tell you anything you want to know.'

'Just what I said.'

'Ah. Just that?' His tone implied disappointment. 'Then, by profession I'm a marine biologist, and by chance, when we were both at Cambridge, I got to know the present Sheikh of Raqat. He's a very liberal, westernised ruler, in spite of your comments which suggest otherwise.'

'Women drivers?' she queried, eyes wide with assumed innocence.

'Of course, he has to move slowly—religious attitudes are deeply ingrained. And I suggest—merely *suggest*—that many western men might have some sympathy—'

'*Don't* say it!'

'All right.' Now he was grinning. 'Provided you don't wave the feminist flag too wildly. It's neither the time nor the place.'

'It's not exactly wild to want to drive yourself in your own car!' With an effort she damped down her excitement, which was more than likely the effect of the alcohol on her brain... 'But please carry on.'

'Thank you.' Grey eyes glittering with laughter seemed to add to her exhilaration; there was a challenging encouragement in them which she must ignore. 'As I was saying, a liberal regime operates here, and has done since oil was discovered.

'You probably know it is a fairly limited field so far; it won't make the sheikhdom enormously rich, but it will make a difference to the people. You can see the benefits even now. But the Sheikh is desperately anxious that the wildlife, especially the marine life in the Red Sea, should not be harmed. So, he contacted me. I took a two-year break from teaching at Princeton to come out here and draw up a plan, give some guidance on a long-term strategy. As I told you, I'm three-quarters through the project now.'

'Oh.' Georgia hadn't come close to identifying Nathan's profession, hadn't once thought of him as an academic. 'It must be fascinating.'

'And exciting,' he added, and she noticed how his manner had changed from slightly laid back to animated. 'I've done a lot of diving but I've never seen a reef with such a variety, such an exciting range of life as the one just to the south of the port. Not even the Australian reefs can compare, and it would be a global tragedy if that breathtaking world should be damaged.' He paused. 'Have you done any diving?'

'A little.' The words were out before she thought to monitor them. She had no wish to let him know that she had belonged to a college sub-aqua team—mainly due to the presence of the man she had been dating then. 'But, it was a long time ago, and I've lost—'

'You can't lose the ability; it's like riding a bike. Besides, it can't be *that* long ago.' By now the food had arrived, and she began to fork up the grainy couscous. 'You're not old enough.'

'Quite old enough.' Georgia had always mistrusted insincere compliments and it was time to change the subject. 'Mmm, this is delicious.'

'I've always liked it. Some of the food is not for the faint-hearted but you can graduate to that in due course. Now you can tell me your real reason for coming to Raqat. The bit about the desert and stars won't wash.'

What point was there in being coy? she thought. Besides, it might not hurt to talk about it. 'The reason, which I'm sure you've guessed, is that I made a complete fool of myself over a man.'

Nat's hand came out, covered hers fleetingly, not giving her time to shrug him off, but it would have been mere pretence to deny the comfort that she found in his gesture. 'That, Georgia, I find hard to believe. Unless he—'

'True, nevertheless,' she cut in before he could say more, then she applied herself to her food.

'I think there must be much more to it, but I shan't probe further.'

'There isn't a lot to say about it, simply that I realised in time what was happening and got out as quickly as I could, but. . .' With her fork she traced some spirals on the couscous while she struggled with the painful memories.

'But?' he prompted, cutting through her musings, giving her the strength to shrug and smile. She even felt and enjoyed the movement of her silk tunic against her skin as she did so—such an. . .arousing experience. . .

'It was just unfortunate that he happened to be my employer.'

'I can see that might make life awkward.'

'It did.' There was a certain defence in turning disaster into a joke. 'I lost the job—*and* the man, which made it doubly annoying.' She raised her glass and sipped. 'And now that incident in the club this afternoon.'

'You were simply unlucky.' Both his expression

and voice were contemplative. 'I'm sure if Grev had been talking to any female, sixteen to sixty, his wife's reactions would scarcely have varied.'

'That, I promise you, doesn't make the memory of it any more pleasant.'

'Of course it doesn't. But, just think, there are large numbers of unattached men here in the sheikhdom.'

'Yes?' It was difficult to see where the conversation was going.

'Yes.' He leaned forward, elbows on the table; he was frowning slightly—whether at her or at the glass he was holding she couldn't decide. 'And you, I hazard a guess, are sure to attract a good deal of attention. Of the Canning variety.'

'So. . .?' She was frowning, disconcerted more by the way his eyes were fixed unswervingly on hers now than by his words, which were casually spoken. 'I think I can deal with anything like that.'

'I believe you—especially after seeing how you dealt with Myra Canning! But. . .wouldn't life be easier for you if footloose males were to imagine. . .well, to put it bluntly, if they thought you were in a regular relationship?'

'Maybe it would be—' she didn't like the direction this discussion was going '—if I were, but. . . I'm not.'

'I know that.' Nat sighed as if she were being singularly obtuse. 'You know that, but no one else needs to.'

'You mean. . .?' The idea was so ridiculous that Georgia laughed. 'You mean that you and I should. . .? But we don't even know each other; I hadn't even seen you until today.'

'Does that matter? Besides, I had seen you several times, even if you had refused to see me.'

'Well, perhaps I did just catch a glimpse of you once. . .'

'I'm grateful for that.'

'I'm sorry.' To her own surprise she giggled. 'But when you're trying to get over a broken heart—' heavens, was she really making a spontaneous joke about it? '—*and* trying to throw off a stomach upset. . .'

'Well, you're over that, judging by how much you've eaten.' Her hissed protest made him grin but he carried on. 'But, as for the broken heart, it might help divert your thoughts to perpetrate a con trick on the ex-pat community here. Besides, imagine how Myra Canning would feel if she thought she had put her foot in it so completely.'

'Well, that might give me a certain amount of unkind pleasure but. . .' Georgia's mind was churning with the effort of trying to balance so many conflicting ideas. 'But. . .' and this was the nub of the matter '. . .I can't see—what is in it for you. You're not, I imagine, so much into philanthropy that you'd risk damaging your reputation to help me out—someone you barely know.'

'Reputation? Well, I doubt if it's worth saving,

but...of course you're right. I do have an interest, rather along the lines of your own in fact; there's someone I want to—how can I put this?—someone I would prefer to discourage.'

'Oh, of course.' It was an irresistible opportunity for sarcasm. 'Men are always being pursued against their inclinations.'

'I didn't say that.' He was amused rather than irritated—that was made clear when he leaned across and touched the tip of her nose with a reproving finger. 'But surely you realise there are times when a man as much as a woman has to deal with unwelcome advances? What I'm suggesting could be the easiest way of going about it. Anyway, that is the proposal. So, what do you say?'

'Well, I suppose...' There was her accommodation to think of; even if an alternative were available she would never be able to afford it. 'It would only be for just two more weeks—'

'Not necessarily,' Nat intervened swiftly. 'It can be for as long as you choose to stay.'

'I think—' hurriedly Georgia made up her mind '—it's a silly idea. I don't for a moment believe I'll be propositioned by anyone.'

'You don't?' The assessing eyes scanned what he could see of her above the table. 'Well, I wouldn't be too sure about that. Especially if you go about dressed like that.'

'What's wrong with this?' It was close to a wail.

'I didn't say anything was *wrong* with it. Rather the reverse. What I was saying was if you go about dressed like that every frustrated male in the territory, and quite a few of the others, will be homing in on you.'

'Oh.' She smiled, blushed, pleased in spite of her normal scepticism with the implied compliment. 'But I wore this specially to. . .'

'Yes?' Nat was laughing. 'You wore it specially to what?'

'Oh. . .' She shrugged, wondering how she had embarked on this particular conversation.

'You do realise—' he leaned across the table '—that lots of men are turned on by—by that particular look?'

'What?' She frowned, the darkly etched eyebrows coming together in a look of concentration. 'I've no idea. . .'

'This.' He tweaked the end of her plait. 'A lot of men find the schoolgirl look irresistible.' The corners of his mouth twitched.

Avoiding Nat's eyes, she raised her glass and stared at it. 'I've always thought that some men have the weirdest hang-ups.'

'Well—' his voice trembled with suppressed amusement '—don't say you weren't warned. Anyway, you began to say something; I'm afraid I distracted you. You wore your present outfit specially to. . .to what?'

'Oh.' She felt the colour begin to rise again. 'I

suppose to give me courage, to soothe my battered ego.' She gave a self-deprecatory shrug. 'You see, when you told me you had a proposal I... I had no idea what you had in mind and... I decided the best thing I could do was to bring out the big guns.'

'I'm very glad you did.' Though he was no longer smiling, there was a warmth about him, a generosity that raised her pulses very slightly. 'So glad,' he went on softly, 'that it seems almost a pity...'

'What?' After a moment Georgia found her voice, which was not easy when his eyes were so compelling, almost mesmeric—but surely that had a lot to do with the reflection of so many flickering candles. 'What seems a pity?' Still she sounded breathy and unfamiliar, as if she had just competed in a hundred-yard dash.

After a seemingly endless pause he answered, and there was something slightly forced about his grin. 'A pity not to show it off a bit more than you've done so far, so why don't we...after we've finished eating...go on to the club? They usually have dancing about this time, so why not embark on the great deception?'

It was strange that his explanation should be such a disappointment. She tried to view the situation with detachment, curious that she was so instantly aware that a rising sense of excitement had to be damped down and... Her eyes searched his face as if trying to discern some flaw. 'You mean—?'

'I mean,' he interrupted, laughing, 'just what I said. Why don't we finish the evening by dropping into the club on the way home? It will give them all a lot to think about.'

'But what if we see Grev there, maybe even his wife?' It was almost a wail.

'So? You're going to bump into them sooner rather than later; in fact I shall be disappointed if they aren't there.'

'I'm not sure I'm ready for it just yet. After all—' it was almost as necessary to remind herself as him '—it was only today that. . .' She frowned in mild disbelief.

'Yeah, it has been quite a day for you, but you're not too tired, are you?'

'No.' The truth was admitted grudgingly. 'I had a long sleep this afternoon.' Sudden amusement produced a smile which dazzled. 'The bed is so much more comfortable than the one downstairs. I was out almost as soon as my head hit the pillow.'

'Then is it decided? I think it would be best. You see, I'm going to Switzerland for a few days, and it would break the ice for you.'

'Switzerland?' For some reason that was all that registered. She would have that lovely, spacious apartment entirely to herself, so why didn't she feel completely euphoric?

'Mmm. A conference.' The discerning grey eyes picked up her look of fleeting desolation before she turned her attention to a distant minaret gleaming in reflected light. 'I would—' Nat's voice was surprisingly gentle '—much rather take you to the club myself than think of you on your own at the mercy of one or two like Myra Canning.' And when she didn't answer he reached out a hand and covered hers. 'So, what's the decision— face the enemy or. . .beat a retreat?'

'Well, since you put it like that. . .' Deftly Georgia did what she ought to have done half a minute before: she removed her hand on the pretext of reaching for her handbag. 'I can hardly refuse!'

'No?' There was an implied question in his voice.

'I'm a soldier's daughter—didn't I tell you? So I guess I'd better do the right thing and face the enemy, like you said.'

'Good girl.' The warm approval had the curious effect of causing a quite distinct throb at the pit of her stomach. Nat rose, holding her chair for a moment while she stood up. 'Over the top it is.'

Then, with a flick of his fingers, he had summoned the waiter while she, Georgia Maitland, stood there looking at him, wondering with a hint of panic what had come over her.

'Shall we go?' His fingers grazed her elbow, but it seemed pointless this time to detach herself.

CHAPTER THREE

THEY parked the car in the grounds of the club, and as they walked along a softly illuminated path towards the foyer Georgia realised that only Nat's touch on her elbow was preventing her from turning tail and running—a knowledge which caused a subtle frisson to run the length of her spine. It wasn't exactly cowardice. At least—she made a correction with a wry private grimace—it wasn't *only* that; it was simply that she'd had enough humiliation in the recent past to last a lifetime.

How silly it was. For a moment she stood unnoticed on the edge of the large room, looking towards the archway to where a lively band was playing. Certainly as far as the Cannings were concerned there was no reason for humiliation— rather the reverse. Whereas with Jordan Severs... Ah, yes, with him it had been quite a different story.

She *ought*—what an idiot—to have suspected, of course, that there might be a wife tucked away somewhere but...well, what could she say? Perhaps simply that she hadn't wanted to know, had deliberately avoided certain questions and...

Tears stung at the back of her eyes; blindly she turned, was caught by the elbows, held firmly. Nat was looking down at her and without doubt noting the tell-tale signs. Now that *was* humiliation. . .

'Steady.' An upward glance showed his mouth curving in a smile entirely sympathetic; he had taken her hand, was pulling her gently, irresistibly towards the dancing. 'Courage.' Then his voice deepened as they threaded a path among crowded tables. 'I'm sure, Georgia, that they're playing our tune.'

That remark, so obviously made for the benefit of whoever might be listening, made her giggle. She didn't resist when he pulled her close, fitting her body into his as they reached the dance floor.

'If this is "our" tune—' her face was against his white shirt-front, the laughter in her voice slightly muffled '—then there are bound to be doubts about our relationship.' Her eyes, when she looked up at him, sparkled with mischief.

'So?'

It was difficult to explain what made her catch her breath—possibly just the endless moment which he took before he continued, his attention lingering on her high cheekbones, the full, tender mouth which gave such character to her face.

And then he said, 'I'm not sure I can identify it.'

'What?' What on earth. . .? Then she remembered. 'Oh, the music, you mean.'

'That *was*, I think, what we were discussing.'

'It's something called "Why doncha trust me, Baby?"' The words rushed out in a hurried gasp. 'It was in the Top Twenty light years ago. I've forgotten the name of the group.'

'Well, that's something to be thankful for! But, on the other hand, the title might be more appropriate than you realise.' It was a joke, of course, and she was quite prepared to smile in mocking appreciation. But his hands slid down till they were resting just above her hips, as their feet moved in unison to the somewhat plaintive beat. 'In fact you shouldn't trust me, baby. Not one inch.'

At that very moment Georgia became conscious of a couple dancing very close, and looked into the eyes of a very judgemental Myra Canning, which made her lose the rhythm completely.

'Well, maybe not.' Excusing her for ruining 'their' tune, Nat pulled her close for a few piquant seconds before, his arm about her waist, he led her from the floor. 'But—' his head was close, his manner intimate '—you carried that off beautifully.'

Then she was swept across to the bar where a small group had congregated, and was introduced to several of his friends—one or two Americans, a couple from New Zealand, others from Britain. The men, she sensed, were friendly; the women, especially one of the Americans, were assessing her carefully from head to toe in a series of slanting glances behind the smiles, taking note of her clothes, her hair, conveying their opinions to each other telepathically as so many women seemed able to do.

Georgia felt herself begin to blush, then remembered that she owed something to Nat and pulled herself together, even managed to place a hand on his arm. She was transfixed when he smiled down at her, captured her hand in his and held onto it—all accomplished as if it were the most natural reaction.

Then she realised how interesting the scene was for the others, in particular the tall American woman whom she had just met. Melanie Jacobs was taking in every detail through narrowed, hostile eyes.

Her interest was so intense that a thought floated, unsought and certainly unwelcome, into Georgia's head. Hadn't Nat spoken about a woman who was disinclined to take a message? So. . .suppose that woman was here, was Melanie? What better opportunity? Nat, she remembered now, had introduced Melanie as an old friend. She was obviously American, and he'd been at Princeton. So what could be more natural?

'Didn't I see you the other night at the Kimberleys'?' her mental sleuthing was interrupted by the voice of a young New Zealander. Dave was all she remembered of his name, but she smiled, mainly because he looked so friendly but also because Melanie was continuing her very persistent summing-up, and this gave her a chance to turn her back.

'Yes. By this time they ought to be in Santiago visiting their daughter.'

'Mmm. And am I right in thinking you've taken the Taylors' apartment while they're on leave?'

'Yes.' The warmth was back in her face, and nothing she could do would halt its progress. In a moment she would blunder into some obviously guilt-racked explanation. In some desperation she looked towards Nat and instantly he was with her, but his support seemed calculated to raise as many eyebrows as was possible.

'There was a mix-up over the arrangements; Pete came back sooner than we expected so we did the obvious thing—Georgia has moved in with me.' Casually he put an arm about her waist, pulling her against him. Just as casually he dropped a light kiss on the top of her head.

It was a corny old idea, the one about wishing that the ground would open up and swallow you, but Georgia suddenly experienced that very desire. And, if Melanie's expression was anything to judge by, what she had heard and the conclusion she had drawn were very unwelcome to her indeed.

It was a relief when there was a diversion. The conversation switched to a discussion about old-time music hall. The topic was generated by the proposed visit of a company from the UK, and at least it gave Georgia time to pull herself together. She was even able to make a couple of sensible comments, both of which—it was very noticeable—were immediately countered by Melanie, who said she just couldn't stand vaudeville.

So, taken all round, it was a relief when a few minutes later Nat indicated that it was growing late and they moved away in a flurry of goodbyes. Georgia very nearly bumped into Grev Canning, who, with his wife, was standing at the bar waiting for service.

'Hi, Grev.' She spoke without thinking, was immediately shocked, then rather pleased that she had acted so spontaneously; she was even able to smile vaguely in the direction of his wife, who looked distinctly uncomfortable.

On the other hand, when Nat stopped to exchange a few words with Grev she was slightly irritated, especially when she heard they were being offered drinks. 'Another time, perhaps, Grev,' said Nat. That was all right, then, she thought. 'We are pretty flaked out and just longing for bed.' And as they walked away Georgia carried the impression of both Grev and his wife staring after them open-mouthed.

The desire to giggle was pretty near irresistible, and she bit fiercely at her lower lip in an effort to repress it, but as they swung through the plate-glass doors she gave up the struggle and gave a little celebratory twirl. 'Yippee.' She waved an imaginary flag, looking up into Nat's face while he stood watching closely, the corners of his mouth turned up, an eyebrow raised questioningly. 'That was. . .fun.' Instinctively she laid her hand flat against his chest.

'Fun?' An intimate reproof. He was holding her about the waist, eyes intent on hers, so that for a second she was afraid that he would kiss her. 'This was a carefully plotted diversion, a ploy to confuse the enemy, not something to be regarded as *fun*.'

'I am *so* sorry,' Georgia mocked, taking the opportunity to move away from him. 'Only, I feel so much better; the awful animosity I felt for Grev's wife has disappeared. That expression on her face. . .' She had another moment's enjoyment then her face grew more sober. 'You think the plan worked, then?'

'Oh, yes.' A touch of grimness now. 'I'm convinced it was a total success.' Something in his tone took her thoughts back to Melanie, reminded her of that particular expression on the American's face when she'd been told that Georgia had moved into the penthouse.

'Melanie.' She tried to find a casual tone but even when she failed had no choice but to continue. 'You did say. . .didn't you, that she was. . . is. . .someone you know well?'

'Mmm.' Something in his manner was detached, noncommital. 'She is what you might call—' here the touch of sarcasm was undeniable '—an old friend of the family.'

All of which seemed to confirm her suspicions—her melancholy suspicions, she told herself as she settled into the car, though why she should be melancholy or suspicious she couldn't explain. Anyway, as they drove along she felt all her earlier euphoria drain out of her; she couldn't even think why she had been so positive and upbeat a few moments before.

She, who had always been so jealous of her reputation, who had never fallen into the habit, practised by so many of her colleagues, of sleeping around, of moving from one man to the next, at the club had been totally complaisant about the opinion which had been deliberately given to the locals.

And given totally without justification, something inside her screamed. Perhaps if she were enjoying the pleasures... She supposed rather sourly that they must be pleasures, otherwise they would be much less popular. Only, she had never been quite able to believe...

So, by the time they had driven through the town and pulled up in front of the block of flats Georgia's uncertainties had reached fever pitch. She was able to contain them while going up in the lift, and while they crossed to the door, but the moment it closed behind them panic over-whelmed her. 'What—what will they think of me?'

'I imagine—' Nat apparently was still mellow and amused '—they'll think exactly what we hoped they would think: that you and I are an item.'

In contrast with his, her voice verged on the shrill. 'That's what I mean.'

'Does it matter much what anyone thinks? Even if it were true, it's scarcely a world-shatter-ing event, and, believe me, in the long run it will save you a lot of hassle.'

'But. . .it's all so contrived, so dishonest.'

'Well. . .' he sighed. She had the impression he might be rapidly tiring of the whole subject; certainly he walked quickly through the hall and into the salon. 'There's an answer to that.' He threw his jacket in the direction of a settee, not pausing to pick it up when it slithered onto the floor. 'Only, I won't complicate matters by draw-ing it to your attention.'

'An answer?' Without thinking she bent to retrieve the jacket, smoothing it once or twice before placing it folded on the back of the seat. Frowning, she stared up into the features which had taken on an impression of deep cynicism, then all at once she understood, and heat and colour suffused her face.

'And don't look so nervous.' Now he was

openly mocking. 'Your virtue is in no way threatened.'

'I'm not.' Inexplicably she was hurt by such an abrupt change of mood. 'And I know it isn't,' she replied to the second point. 'Please don't treat me like a naïve teenager.'

'Then don't act like one.' Nat had turned away, was busy with bottles. He poured a glass of tonic water, offered it to her with a raised eyebrow, and she refused with a swift sideways move of her head. He moved, supporting himself against one of the pillars which led out onto the balcony, surveying her, studying her with slow, insulting detachment before raising his glass and draining it.

'I didn't realise I was.' Georgia's voice shook with controlled passion. How wonderful, she thought, if she could have thought of some utterly cutting remark, but as ever in such circumstances her mind remained obstinately blank.

Then, since he showed no sign of wishing to continue any sort of conversation and since. . .she swallowed a sob. . .since everything about him indicated regret that he had ever become involved with her, she turned and reached the door. 'Well, once again, thank you for such an. . .such an interesting evening and. . .goodnight.'

'Oh.' He frowned, put down his glass and took a step forward. 'Yes, you must be tired, and so am I. And. . . I did tell you. . . I'm off tomorrow to Basle. One of those conferences—' his smile was slightly grim '—where everyone is so concerned about the future of the planet that they fly in from every corner, not noticing how many resources are used up in the process.'

'How. . .how long will you be away?'

'Four days at the outside, so you can relax completely, treat the flat as your own. Enna will look after you, and should you want to be driven anywhere then just tell Ismail.'

'Thank you. I'll try not to be too much trouble.'

'Now don't be too meek and self-effacing.' Apparently recovered from his momentary sharpness, he smiled, coming across to where she stood in the doorway. 'It doesn't suit you.' Resting one hand on the door, he leaned forward and gave her pigtail a gentle tug with the other. 'It would be too out of character.'

'Really?' She had no intention of chopping and changing moods to suit him, so her tone was saccharine sweet. 'I'm so glad I didn't waste money on a character analysis before I came, because you're doing such an excellent job.'

'Accurate, would you say?'

'Contradictory.' It was impossible now to repress a smile, even though it was edged with exasperation. 'Naïve teenager one moment, devious and self-promoting the next.'

'Did I say that?'

'Something close.'

'Then you must forgive me. I'm not usually so rude.'

'Now, that is a surprise.' She was being deliberately provocative and her mouth quivered when he laughed delightedly.

'I deserved that. I simply gave way to a momentary. . .irritation, shall I call it?'

'If it's that, why hesitate? It's a condition most of us suffer from time to time.'

'There are reasons for avoiding a more precise word but. . .so long as I'm forgiven.'

'Well. . .since I'm living in your house, on sufferance I'll have to toe the line. . .' Georgia had always enjoyed light-hearted repartee, especially when, as now, there was an edge of. . .what was it?. . .of flirtation! Was it possible?

'Might be diplomatic,' Nat was agreeing.

It was definitely time to change both the tone and the subject. Besides, this was something they ought to have discussed at the beginning, 'Oh, you must tell me what I owe for rent and food and. . .for everything.'

'Forget it.'

'I couldn't possibly.'

'Now you're being prim, also out of character. But, if it makes you feel any better, *I* don't pay for the flat; it's all provided courtesy of the Sheikh. He owns the block and has given me the place rent-free. So, you see, it would be highly unethical if I were to charge *you*.'

'Which puts me more and more in *your* debt.'

'Naturally. That's my plan. Don't say you didn't suspect! In a moment I'll be back to my first assessment. . .'

'You'd still be wrong.'

'Tell me.' Suddenly he became more serious. Head on one side, he studied her closely. 'Tell me, what really brought you out here, Georgia? I'm not entirely convinced by your story about having made a fool of yourself over a man.'

'It's a common enough story, after all.' There was the faintest taint of bitterness in her tone. 'Haven't women always been doing just that?'

'Maybe. At one time or another most of us make fools of ourselves. But *you*. And over a man. I find it hard to believe.'

'Well, thank you for your vote of confidence.' She smiled self-deprecatingly. 'So what makes me different from the rest of my sex? I can't—'

'Looks. Personality. Style.' Nat was eyeing her closely. 'I could go on.' It was perverse of her to be disappointed that he didn't. 'You said something about your employer. . .' It was a gentle prompting to which she responded reluctantly.

'Ye-es.' It had been a mistake to admit as much earlier on, and yet it was easier to contemplate telling him than she would have believed. 'It was one of those stupid situations. Really, you'd think that at twenty-six I would be less gullible, wouldn't you?'

There was a challenge in the enormous eyes gazing up at him, and when he nodded briefly she went on. 'I'd worked with him for about six months. At the time it seemed such a wonderful opportunity—to be taken on by one of London's top fashion houses. It was so flattering, the way he made me think my designs were miles ahead of anyone else's. He rushed me—swept me off my feet, to use an overworked phrase.'

She smiled cynically. 'And I was naïve enough—oh, yes, exactly like that silly teenager you mentioned; come to think of it, that could be why I disliked the comparison so much—to fall madly in love with him. It was the merest chance that I discovered he had a wife and family tucked away in the country.' She gnawed savagely at her lower lip, turned abruptly to conceal any brightness in her eyes and laughed briefly with a quick shrug of her shoulders. 'And that was that.'

Only, that wasn't quite that, she admitted privately as restlessly she crossed the room and stepped out onto the terrace, leaning forward on the balcony rail to take in the view of the town garlanded with lights, which in turn were reflected in the distant sea. Not for worlds would she share the trauma that she had endured when, in response to a sudden emergency, she had tried to trace him, had found herself talking first of all to his daughter, then to his wife, with the sound of a crying infant underlining an impression of domestic harassment.

'Charlotte, run up to my bedroom; tell Daddy someone is on the telephone for him.'

She had still been in a state of shock when Jordan at last had come on the line. She'd passed on the message and then added, 'Oh, and Jordan—' she could recall just how thick her voice had sounded '—forget about Antigua. I had no idea you had other commitments.'

'There's no need for that,' he'd said, and then in a more muffled tone, 'I can't talk right now, Georgia; surely you can see that? I'll ring you when it's more convenient.'

'I think your wife has prepared your breakfast, Jordan; I swear I can smell the bacon grilling.' After hanging up the telephone she had collected all her belongings, including her design portfolio, and had returned to her studio flat.

Naturally Jordan had called back. She had listened in silence as he'd tried to persuade her to change her mind largely, she was convinced, because he did not want to risk forfeiting the cost of the holiday.

'But it needn't be wasted, Jordan.' Georgia had been all sweetness. 'You can always take someone else. Your wife, perhaps.'

'Don't be ridiculous.'

'Well, why not Wendy?' It had been his secretary, who had produced the home telephone number and Georgia had had time to wonder why it had been pushed into her hand with such alacrity. Once or twice she had caught an odd look on the older woman's face. 'I have the idea that she would be more than willing to overlook the fact of your wife and children.'

Quietly she'd put the receiver down on the table, walking swiftly away before she could lose control and scream like a fishwife, and she had no idea how long he'd stood talking to himself. Just three days later she'd flown out to Raqat.

Nat had followed her, was close by, leaning against the balustrade, but unlike her he showed little interest in the view; all his attention was on her profile. 'You will get over it, I promise you.'

With a quick grin she turned her head in his direction. 'You reckon?' Again she turned towards the town.

'I reckon! We all have things. . .' some note in his voice drew her attention again '. . .things we regret, things that ought not to have happened. . .'

'That's true.' Had he been about to confide some trouble of his own? She couldn't say, but at that moment she wasn't in the mood to listen. She knew that if she didn't make her escape pretty quickly she was in imminent danger of making a complete fool of herself. 'But now—' her voice shook with the effort of control '—I must go to bed before I flake out completely. It has, to put it mildly, been a long, long day.'

'Sure.' He walked with her through to the main hallway where they paused. 'Goodnight, Georgia. Sleep well.' His head bent and she felt the touch of his mouth against her cheek, worried that he might taste saltiness there and draw his own conclusions.

'Thank you, Nat. You just about saved my life today and I shan't forget that. Goodnight.' She remembered about his trip to Switzerland. 'Oh, shall I see you in the morning?'

'I doubt it; I'll be off pretty early. But remember what I said—make the most of Enna and Ismail while I'm away. And when I come back I plan to take you on a diving expedition.'

About that she was less than certain. As she splashed her face with warm water in the bathroom she decided she was too much out of practice to take part in that kind of scheme. But, she thought, looking at her reflection as she dabbed herself with a soft, fleecy towel, she had something else on her mind—a recollection which brought a surge of emotion to her stomach, disturbing in its implications.

In that moment when Nat had bent to touch her skin in the most chaste of goodnight kisses— the kind of caress with which you said goodbye to an elderly maiden aunt—his mouth seemed to have imprinted itself on her cheek. She had had to force herself to resist an inclination—no, much more than that—an urge, a potent desire—to lean against him, perhaps even to link her arms about his neck.

Which would have shocked the poor man completely, would have forced him to a hurried retreat behind his bedroom door. His *locked* bedroom door! She determined to turn the idea into a light-hearted joke, but it didn't quite come off.

There was still this feeling of warm astonishment in recalling that suffusion of quick pleasure when his mouth had touched her cheek. For a long time she lay in the near-darkness pondering the significance of her reaction without coming up with a satisfactory answer.

Other recollections intruded, equally puzzling: the shock waves when his hand had accidentally brushed against her bare skin—oh, a dozen times that had happened in the course of one short evening—the scent of male cologne, which had never been so arousing. And the one he wore, she knew, would always be associated with one special evening in her life. And that was the night—she was determined to find an explanation which was cool and acceptable—when she had finally got Jordan Severs out of her system. For that she would always be grateful to Nathan Trehearn. Relieved that she had solved the problem, she sighed deeply, and as she drifted off to sleep one slender finger safeguarded an exact spot on her cheek.

CHAPTER FOUR

IN A WAY Georgia enjoyed the few days on her own. It was so comfortable and relaxed, and certainly it made a great difference to life when you had a vehicle constantly at your disposal. And Ismail, in contradiction of his condescending air, was anxious to be helpful, driving her to parts of the old quarter of Raqat which she would never have found by herself.

Happily she would sit for hours on her own, free to indulge her old teenage hobby, neglected in the serious task of earning a living, of sketching—ancient whitewashed buildings, narrow, secret passageways, brilliantly domed mosques into which the faithful streamed at certain times of the day. It was all so totally fascinating, so refreshingly distinctive.

What the driver did during these spells she didn't discover, and imagined he might have gone back to help Enna with the chores, though she did catch sight of him once. He was in a group of men sitting in the shady courtyard of a coffee-shop, all drinking coffee, arguing, clicking beads as the problems of the world were solved.

A few rapid strokes of her crayon and Georgia

had caught the essence of the man—the curling black hair beneath the oval velvet cap, the hooked nose, the firmly etched eyebrows. Mmm... She held her sketch at arm's length for a critical moment. He was clearly recognisable. Another few touches suggested the other figures about the table, and when she carelessly presented it to him on the way home his pleasure and delight were touching.

But much of her time was spent sitting in the main shopping street—a real melting pot. Peasants from the interior were disgorged from buses to mingle with the most sophisticated jet-setters as they shopped for the latest thing in designer goods.

As well as her sketch-pad she used her camera here, to capture more of the elusive shades than she thought her brain could retain. All the subtle browns and creams of earth and sand mingled with and absorbed brilliant greens and blues, and she was entranced by a particularly unusual yellow—citrus with just a hint of London fog— which could look wonderfully subtle and diaphanous.

Still, it was dismaying, in a pleasurable way, to find herself excited at the prospect of Nat's return—more dismaying still to take a call and hear his voice at the other end telling her of a delay. More even than that, it was sharply disappointing.

'I'm sorry, Georgia. I've had to stop off unexpectedly in Cairo.'

'Oh, *no*!' How ridiculous; she sounded like a wife who had been slaving for hours over a welcoming meal.

'Yeah. Another short consultation, but it means I'll have to spend the night here.'

'What a nuisance for you.' That was much better; she had no intention of letting him know how much trouble she had taken. A glance in the mirror in front of her showed long, gleaming hair, subtle make-up, an understated, elegant skirt and filmy blouse. 'Anyway, thanks for letting me know. I'll pass the information on to Enna. . .'

'Everything all right?'

'Yes, fine. Ismail has been really helpful, taking me all round the city and showing me all the sights.'

'Good. Well. . .' Was he reluctant to break off the contact or was that sheer self-deceit? Just because she was hyped up that didn't mean he too. . .

'Oh, I spoke to Pete Taylor. He called the other day before he went off to the airport to pick up his wife.' When Nat came back tomorrow she would tell him that Pete had said he would repay some of the money she had paid for the flat. 'He wanted to know if I was all right.'

'And. . .?'

'And of course I told him I was prepared to put

up with the luxury of the penthouse, the responsibility of the servants and the car.'

At that he laughed; she felt herself grow warm
with pleasure. 'It has been pretty rough on you,'
he said.

'Very.'

'Well, from tomorrow I intend to change all
that. You're going to have to earn your penthouse
accommodation. I'll be back on an early flight
and—no excuses—we'll go diving off the reef.'

'Oh, Nat, I'm not sure about that. It's ages
since—'

'No, but I *am* sure, so be ready. I have a heavy
diary later in the week and I always find it the
perfect way to relax. We can take some films
which I guarantee will inspire you for the next ten
years.'

'Well. . . I'm not convinced that fish will provide—'

'They will dazzle, fire the imagination. Until
you've seen the colours, wondered at the movement—'

'All right, you've convinced me. I promise I'll
be ready.'

'Good girl. Now, I must go—I'm being paged.
See you at—oh, let's say at dawn tomorrow.'

'But isn't that when they fight duels?'

His laughter was soft, intimate. 'Goodnight,
Georgia. Sleep well.' The curious little flop in her

stomach was down to the tenderness—just a hint of it—in the deep, mellow voice.

'Goodnight, Nat.' She sounded breathless. There was no other way of describing it. Breathless and soft and. . .indulgent was the only other word which came to mind.

When she had replaced the receiver she wandered out onto the terrace, filled now, in the still darkness, with all the exotic scents of the East. She felt at once disappointed and tremendously excited. She could not recall that the prospect of diving off the coast at Aberystwyth had ever generated such anticipation, but then Cardigan Bay and the Red Sea were as far apart as her instructors. Nat Trehearn was in a different league altogether from Richard. But then Nat Trehearn was in a league all of his own.

Wrinkling her nose in amusement at such adolescent musings, she turned abruptly away. She had promised to let Enna know of the changed plans, so had better do so instead of standing here dreaming.

The following day only confirmed the thoughts of the previous night: diving in the Red Sea had little connection with the same activity off the Welsh coast. The immediate advantage was that with the water so warm and clear there was no need to be burdened with a wet suit and, point number two, Nat Trehearn was confidently expert in a way that Richard had not been. She might have guessed.

There was casual confidence in everything he did—his handling of the boat as they slipped out of the harbour, the easy way he pointed out geographical detail as they travelled down the coast. But it was difficult for Georgia to hide from herself that it was the individual, the physical man, whom she found so interesting, rather than his abilities.

She was disturbed by the way his checked shirt fell open to the waist. She who in her career had become as familiar with the unclothed male figure as with the female was affected by the deeply tanned chest with its sprinkling of silky hair; in fact it was becoming increasingly difficult for her to look elsewhere.

Restlessly she moved her seat, then reached into her bag for her sketching-pad, referring to him in snatched glances while she transferred his outline to the paper.

'Nearly there.' Nat's quick, slanting look took her by surprise, and she was grateful for the sunglasses which she hoped might have disguised her interest. But then, trying to concentrate on her drawing, she knew that he in turn was taking in details of her appearance—hair today caught back in a wide band, face bare of make-up, two-piece swimsuit—not a bikini but a stretchy sports top and matching briefs, surely more suitable for diving.

Though when she had caught sight of her reflection before leaving the flat there had been a moment's panic. A plain black two-piece had no right to be so seductive! It was meant to be sensible, businesslike. Hastily she'd pulled on a loose blouse, which offered some disguise but unfortunately did nothing to disguise the length of her legs.

'Right.' He was close enough to startle. She placed the pad face down on the seat, unable to explain why she hadn't noticed the engine being switched off. 'Let me help you on with this gear.'

There was no choice but to discard the blouse, to allow him to adjust the straps of the oxygen tank, and she found herself exercising iron control as his fingers smoothed the webbing over her skin, checking for comfort. And he was frowning as he checked the fit of her mask. She felt her heart hammering against her chest, blood thundering in her ears.

When he bent to check on her flippers, hands grazing against her instep, she could have screamed, though luckily, as far as she could judge, he remained wholly detached. It was a relief when he had finished his inspection and she was free to stare out over the sea, forcing herself to breathe slowly, steadily, until her pulse-rate had returned to something approaching normal.

· 'Ready?' When he spoke she was able to fix a grin, obeying his instructions to position herself on the side of the boat, to pull down her mask and breathing tube and, at his signal, to slew backwards into the water. A second's panic and she discovered that Nat had been right when he'd told her that, like riding a bike, it wasn't the kind of thing you forgot. But she was glad of the hand he held out and the guidance he gave as they swam towards the reef.

But nothing he had said, nothing in her wildest imagination had prepared Georgia for the world that she was now visiting. Even the most descriptive film could hardly do justice to such beauty.

From time to time her companion would draw her attention to one spectacular aspect or another, even producing a little board and waterproof marker to clarify matters. And, sure enough, she could just about make out the shape of a sunken ship under the layers of coral deposits.

A shoal of transparent fish emerging suddenly from the drunkenly angled funnel startled her; she recoiled, felt his arms come about her, but with a flick of her feet she drew away, raising a hand in apology. 'Glass fish' he scribbled on his board as another shoal came swirling towards them, then changed direction abruptly as if they were controlled by one brain, wheeling and darting in exquisite choreography.

Idly, hand in hand, they circled the wreck, Nat pulling her back as a giant jellyfish fluttered its tentacles in their direction before rippling off into the distance. Then they trod water to watch as chevron barracuda began a breathtaking spiral display. Wonderful, dazzling, weird shapes darted, swam, floated, rotated till her brain was throbbing with stimulation and excitement.

When they surfaced and she was helped aboard, she collapsed onto a seat, pulled off her mask and reached for the clips so that she could get rid of her tank. 'That was simply breathtaking. I—'

'Let me help you. They can be awkward when the straps are wet.' But not for Nat; the task was soon accomplished. 'So—' a dark eyebrow was raised, hair swept back from his face by raking fingers '—it was worthwhile?'

'Oh, yes. I would never have believed. . . Thank you, Nat, for taking me.'

His eyes, gazing down at her, held a strange expression and, barely moving, he reached for a towel which he handed to her. 'It was a pleasure, I promise you.' Idly he rubbed his own towel across his chest. The faint rasp left her giddy for a second, then he draped it about his shoulders and half turned. 'And for a girl who tried to chicken out you did pretty well.'

'Did I?' It was absurd to feel this pleased at such an automatic and probably meaningless compliment, idiotic to feel her cheeks grow hot. 'Well, it is much easier here.' She rubbed the front of her head with the towel, felt more composed when facing him again. 'So warm, and the water's like crystal, but still, I was amazed at so many beautiful creatures. Do you know them all by name? The species, I mean.' She grinned, relieved that she could be so casual. 'Not the individuals.'

'Most of them. I'll begin teaching you the names when we go in again.' He reached into the cool-box that they had brought and produced two cans. 'Feel like a drink?'

'Thanks.' She pulled the ring and drank thirstily. 'That's good.'

'If I were you I'd sit under the awning. The heat can be ferocious at this time of day, especially when you're not used to it. And, if you like, if you're not too tired, we can go back down when we've had something to eat.'

They had finished rolls and salad and were enjoying a cup of iced coffee when Georgia said reflectively, 'Sad, isn't it, seeing that wreck resting on the reef?'

'Mmm. There are hundreds of wrecks, perhaps even thousands, lying along the bottom. Even before the canal was built this was a busy shipping route; trade between Egypt, Arabia and the East has always flourished.'

'You. . .' Looking up into his face, she confirmed what she already knew—that his eyes were on her. But it was their expression which brought confusion; her mind became totally blank and she was unable to recall what had been in her thoughts a mere second before. And all simply because she recognised that special look of sexual awareness. . .

But always in the past she had remained aloof—until the recent bungled affair with Jordan, that was. But even then. . .even then she had remained immune to this sudden, lurching, stomach-churning response. 'You. . .' she began again, and again the word trailed away.

Nat was smiling at her, slowly, intently and with a hint of tenderness. There was a sparkle in the eyes searching her features so closely, as if suggesting they were close to enlightenment. And then, still slowly—she had the feeling that her life had changed to a lower gear, giving her much more time to experience so many new sensations—he leaned forward and touched his mouth to hers.

Time stopped then. Only for a moment and yet she was so blindingly alive to a whole host of weaknesses previously discounted. With her eyes half-closed, she could see the countours of his chest, ached with the urge to raise fingertips to trace the muscles beneath the bronzed skin. It was imagination—of course it was—to sense her pulses racing in rhythm with his, to feel the surge of electric power through both bodies and. . .

'I. . .?' Now he was looking down, a finger reaching out to skim the curve of her cheek. 'I. . .? I what?'

'What?' she repeated stupidly, bewildered before her mind cleared and blessed relief came; she laughed at her own incompetence. 'I *was* going to say, you seem to know such a lot. . .'

'How very perceptive of you.'

'Seriously.' Now under assault from so many emotions, she tried to detach herself from them and deliberately selected a tiny pastry which she ate thoughtfully before going on. 'You seem to be immersed—' her choice of word brought a giggle 'literally—in all aspects of marine life.'

'Well. . .it's all I've ever known. I've been diving since I was about seven; it's in the blood, you see. My great-grandfather started in the marine salvage business about a hundred years ago, and with present-day technology the possibilities are endless.

'TMI, Trehearn Marine International, was the company which salvaged that Spanish treasury galleon in the West Indies last year, and we're into oil exploration, oceanography—everything to do with the oceans. But my special interest, my hobby as well as my profession, is trying to protect the marine life as much as possible in an increasingly hungry world.'

'Oh?' It was a new and bewildering aspect of Nat's life and background; even she had heard of

Trehearn Marine. 'But I thought you said you lectured at Princeton.'

'That's right. I'm fortunate to have had so many opportunities. My father is a pretty fit man and has always thrived on running the company, but. . .he's now beginning to hint at handing over some of the responsibilities, and that means one thing only—I've got to take over the reins.'

'I see. And how will you like that?'

'Oh. . .' He gave a little laugh with more than a hint of bitterness, and for a moment his attention appeared to drift. His eyes focused on the far horizon, but then they snapped back to look at her. 'I've always known what was expected of me. And that, I promise you, is not always an enviable position.'

He smiled and shrugged. 'But now—' he began competently to collect and stow away the remains of their lunch '—I think we should sail a few miles south; there's an even more spectacular reef I would like you to see.'

'I doubt that.' Georgia busied herself with the clips and buckles of her diving equipment. 'I can imagine nothing more spectacular than we have seen so far.'

'I promise you. . .' There was no way she could escape the domination of his manner. Her heart was hammering against her ribs; she would have sworn she heard the blood singing in her veins. 'I promise you—' Nat's voice was lower, softer '—a

glimpse of paradise. I promised myself the very
first time I saw you—' his mouth curved a little at
the corners '—that I would be the one to show it
to you.'

Time was suspended while they stood staring at
each other. Georgia was aware of her quick,
shallow breathing through slightly open lips,
aware that his eyes were centred on them till,
with a contrite little shrug which seemed to apologise for their cumbersome equipment, he turned
away.

For the rest of the afternoon, hand in hand with
Nat, Georgia allowed herself to be led, floating,
skimming, drifting with and through shoals in
vivid, mind-blowing colours, from time to time
attempting to merge with their balletic sequences
while Nat captured them on film. It was such
intense, perfect pleasure that his words kept
repeating in her brain, and she knew that just to
glimpse paradise would not be enough for her.
She determined to *be* there, experiencing the joy
of being alone with Nat.

Watching that powerful, athletic figure skimming through the water towards her, Georgia
knew that she had never met anyone like Nat
Trehearn. And instinct told her that if paradise
could be glimpsed here on earth he was the man
who would take her there.

CHAPTER FIVE

GEORGIA woke from her nap on a high. Immediately recognising that incredible fact, she lay for a moment, quite still, savouring, marvelling, enjoying the unaccustomed physical pleasure of the state before allowing her mind to investigate.

Her first idea, which she immediately cast aside, was that her euphoria had something to do with diving. Fascinating though that had been, there must be some other reason, another explanation for her sudden change of character. Flirtatiousness simply wasn't her style and yet, driving back to the flat with Nat after the diving lesson, one might have thought. . .

Ah, yes, best to face it, she thought. Therein most probably lay the entire explanation, for until this point in her life she had not known Nat Trehearn! Simple! A smile touched her mouth, innocent yet a trifle smug, and the green eyes which an instant earlier had widened in shocked surprise drifted closed as she allowed imagination to take over.

She gave a languid stretch, relaxation travelling the length of her body while her mind was fixed on that other body, taut and male, deeply bronzed and contoured—fixed so tantalisingly that a tiny moan of frustration escaped her lips. She turned in the bed and buried her face in the pillow.

Then a glance at the bedside clock reminded her of time passing. She ought to think of dressing, and besides, there was the chance that she might be expected to help preparing the meal. That thought made her pause; excitement began again to stir at the pit of her stomach. No Ismail, no Enna this evening. The chaperons—her safety net, as initially she had seen them—would be for the first time removed. . .

If she was to be helping in the kitchen something plain and practical should be chosen from her wardrobe—jeans and T-shirt, say, and not, *not* that favourite dress. But still, it was towards that delicious garment that her fingers reached out when she rose—the dress which had been in her thoughts ever since Nat, driving back with her in the car after the diving expedition, had explained that the servants were taking time off for some family celebration.

And the dress *was* fairly simple. How easy it was to lie, to convince herself as she did a little pirouette in front of her reflection. The *line* was simple—nothing could be simpler than an A-line dress swaying from narrow rouleau straps. All the sophistication, and—she would be foolish to deny it—all the luxury lay in the sheerness of the silks and the subtlety of the shadings, from palest eaude-nil across the bust to a froth of deep sea-green at the calf-length hem. A gold lining shimmered and gleamed with every move she made.

It suited her. She determined not to allow herself to be carried away, but even when she turned from the mirror to pick up her make-up the image would not be wiped from her mind. Maybe it had something to do with the brush of the silk against bare skin—skin just a little more sensitive than usual after a day in the sea. Light, deft touches of make-up, scarcely necessary when she had taken on such a honeyed glow, resulted in greeny eye-shadow, a hint of gold on the lashes, a glossy brownish pink to her mouth.

But what was more—she gave another critical, *detached* look at herself—the dress suited her *mood*. In sudden joy she wrapped her arms about herself and spun round. It suited her mood of devilish, abandoned femininity, which she was sure she was going to find addictive. Addictive? A slender, interrogative eyebrow was raised, answered by a mischievous grin. Well, what was wrong with being addicted to flirtation and femininity?

A negative head movement tried to damp down her expectations, but it merely swirled her hair around her head in glossy swathes, and in despair she reached for her atomiser. A swift blast over shoulders and throat, and she walked from the bedroom in a waft of Balenciaga.

'Hi.' Busy in the kitchen when she reached it, Nat swung round at her greeting, his eyes taking in every detail of her appearance in a single approving glance.

'Hi.' That deep, mellow drawl—it too could easily become addictive; certainly that was what the yearning surge in the pit of her stomach was saying. 'You look. . .'

'Overdressed?' A nervous interjection was her attempt to damp down feelings which were verging on the unstable. 'I did wonder if this was a bit over the top for a quiet evening at home.'

'It's perfect.' Half turning, he produced a tray with glasses and a hazy, chilled bottle. 'You look stunning; I don't for a moment suppose you need me to tell you that.' Smiling, he directed her through the salon and onto the balcony, lit by cunningly concealed lamps. Offering her a glass across the small table, he grew more serious. 'Nevertheless I shan't deny myself the pleasure of saying you look beautiful.'

'Thank you.' It was an assurance she had heard before but never with this devastating effect; a sip of cool wine did nothing to subdue her feelings.

'Your own work?' He glanced over her bare shoulders and as much of the rest of the dress as was visible above the table.

'Mmm. At least, my own design. I didn't actually *make* it.'

'No, I suppose not. I tend to imagine dress

designers slaving for hours over sewing machines, but I guess I've got it all wrong.'

'Just a bit.' She grinned. 'But, if you're being competely honest, I don't imagine it has ever occurred to you to wonder how we artistic folk work.'

'Well. . .' He shrugged, raised an amused eyebrow.

'As I thought.'

'Well, let's say, dress designing is to me what marine biology is to you.'

'I'm not going to admit to that. But anyway, to a certain extent you are right. During our training we had to produce our own designs, from drawing-board to coat-hanger, but I can't say I enjoyed that side too much. I was always more interested in the history of fashion. That tied in with the history degree I took before doing the course in designing.'

'I see. Well, as you've gathered, I'm pretty clueless about all that.'

'You surprise me.' About to say that his clothes always gave her the impression of someone who had at least one eye on fashion, she changed her mind, deciding he wasn't a man to be impressed by flattery.

Nevertheless, even now, there was a certain style about the dark cotton trousers, the fuchsia-red silk shirt with wide sleeves. Nat was the very essence of clothes-conscious late twentieth-century man. She watched him rake back from his forehead a lock of glossy sable hair. And those clothes combined with those dark Byronic looks. . . He was much more attractive, she had to confess, than she had noticed in the early days of their acquaintanceship. That deep V of bronzed skin at the open neck of his shirt made her fingers simply itch.

'Do I?' His interruption at such a crucial moment in her contemplation brought colour rushing back into her cheeks—a phenomenon which appeared to interest him considerably, but at last he took pity on her dilemma.

'For some reason, I surprise you,' he explained.

'Oh, that. I thought you would have known all about clothes design and manufacture. As I told you before, you seem to *know* such a lot.'

'Well, I'll have to see what I can do about introducing it to my students.'

'I'm sure they would find it relevant. Oh, and—' it was time to change the subject '—you mentioned slaving over a sewing machine. I was prepared to help with the meal, to slave over a hot stove, should that be necessary, even to—'

'Which it isn't.' Draining his glass, he rose. 'Since Enna left a fridge packed with food. So, if you're as hungry as I am, maybe we should eat.'

When they reached the dining room, the impression was one of intimacy—pink linen, the only illumination from candles, posies of sweet-smelling flowers at each place-mat. She allowed him to hold her chair, waited while he served chilled soup and took his seat opposite.

'Expert waiter as well?'

'As well as what? I ask myself.' Then, without waiting for an answer, he went on, 'I did the usual stint in a burger bar while I was at college.'

'Oh?' She tasted the delicious concoction of tomatoes with herbs and yoghurt and broke off a piece of roll. 'I thought only poor kids did that—worked their way through college, I mean.'

'Well, I *was* a fairly poor student at one time. Dad didn't believe in spoiling us. What about you? Didn't you work in the holidays?'

'Sometimes I did. Would you believe—' the unexpected recollection made her giggle and reach for her drink '—I did a spell in a chicken-packing factory once?' She sipped from her glass and raised eyes which sparkled with mischief. 'We all stood at an assembly line snapping elastic bands round dead birds.'

'Sounds like fun.'

'It was disgusting. But it did have its lighter side. One of the women there had a very active love life, and each morning we were regaled with details of what had taken place the previous night—soap opera for very adult listeners. I never quite made up my mind if it was simply a case of an overactive imagination, but it certainly helped to take one's mind off the cadavers.'

'Beats the burger bar any day of the week. It didn't turn you vegetarian?'

'No, not quite.' It had crossed her mind that that period might have had an effect on her sex life, but this was not the time to go into that. 'I don't think I was there long enough for it to have a lasting effect.'

They had begun to eat lamb kebabs with salad. 'You said your father was in the army; did that mean a lot of moving about?'

It was a subject she avoided when she could but she found herself saying, 'Not really. You see, my parents divorced when I was quite young and then I went away to boarding-school when I was nine. My sister is eight years older so it didn't affect her so much. While I was growing up I spent the holidays with my mother and stepfather.

'But three years ago I did have a wonderful few months with Dad when he was stationed in Australia and I was able to go out there in the summer. Since then I've grown closer to Dad. He's retired now, back in England, and I visit him quite a lot, but I'm fond of them all. My mother and stepfather live in Scotland, and Penny, my sister—she got married a few years back. She's in Wales. What about you? Any brothers or sisters?'

'No.' Almost immediately she wished she had not asked, as his expression grew sombre. He rose and began to collect plates. 'At least—' making an obvious effort, he produced a tight little smile

'—I did have a brother, younger than I; he was killed in a skiing accident in the Rockies.'

'Oh. . . I'm so sorry.' All the questions with which she might have pursued the subject remained unasked; Nat's pain was so obvious. And when he returned from the kitchen with the coffee and they went into the sitting room she moved on to something else; there was no way she wanted the mood of the evening, till then so amiable but with a quite distinct undertow of sexual attraction, to change.

'Thank you again, Nat.' This seemed a safe topic. 'It was a wonderful experience this afternoon.' Her brilliant green eyes surveyed him over the rim of her coffee-cup. How, she asked herself, had she ever come to the absurd conclusion that he wasn't handsome? Not conventionally so, perhaps, but he was staggeringly attractive. 'It was kind of you to take me.'

'You think I was being *kind*?' he asked in a tone of amused wonder.

'You make it sound like an insult.' She enjoyed light-hearted backchat, especially when there was this edge of awareness between them. His warm, sardonic glance made heat burn through her again, and she lowered her eyes as she put her cup carefully down on the table. 'But I think it's a fair comment, given that you took me under your wing when I was in a jam and *then* went out of your way to entertain me.'

'Remember what I told you when we first met?' He came to stand beside her, tilted her face upwards, brushed a thumb over her mouth. 'If I hadn't, then you would have had a queue of men only too willing to help you explore the pleasures of. . .of Raqat. Anyway—' his hand dropped '—it's a pity I'm going to be so tied up for the next few days; it looks like we'll have to wait till next week before we can continue our exploration of the reef.'

Next week? A tiny shiver ran down her spine, but it seemed the wrong moment to tell him that her flight home was booked for Monday, the wrong moment for her even to contemplate. . .

The sitting room was dim and mysterious, the only light spilling in from the veranda, throwing shadows across walls and furnishings.

Georgia felt herself cocooned in the depths of the pale soft leather settee, all her senses seduced and tormented by the beguiling sound of the background music that Nat had put on. She had no idea what it was, just that it was causing havoc—there were so many haunting chords and strings. And when Nat moved from his seat opposite, sat beside her, draping an arm along the back of the sofa, she acted against her most powerful instincts and withdrew slightly into the corner.

'You shouldn't let this guy—' he spoke drily, idly brushing a hand against her bare shoulder

'—the one you told me about—make you think all men are predators.'

'No.' The laugh she was able to summon had little conviction; she wondered if he could hear her heart's wild beating. 'I don't. Of course I don't.'

'I wasn't about to pounce.'

'No?' Intending to make a sardonic query, she heard instead a desolate note, implying a regret which would endure till doomsday.

'Well. . .' Without turning her head she knew that his attention was concentrated on her profile; she felt a strap slip from her shoulder, shivered as his fingers moved to replace it and lingered against the sensitive skin. 'What am I supposed to make of that?'

'Nothing.' Irritated with herself—surely at twenty-six one ought not to be so gauche?—and frustrated—for heaven's sake, why not admit as much?—she got up, took a few aimless steps away and swung round. 'Nothing.' Disappointment and accusation mingled in her voice. 'You're supposed to make nothing of it.'

'Tell me, Georgia. . .' Lazily Nat got to his feet and followed her; a slant of light distorted his strong features and they suggested, just for a split second, that he was the hunter, she the quarry. Or was this more wishful thinking? she asked herself with a crazy illogicality. 'Is it still too painful to talk about?'

'What?' He had lost her; her brain was too much involved with a wild, exciting chase through woods. 'I'm sorry, I. . .'

'This man—the one who gave you such a hard time.' Now he was edgy and impatient. 'The one who broke your heart so you had to rush across continents in search of a cure.'

'Oh, that.' She ignored his touch of sarcasm, waved her hand and gave a sudden grin, which was largely relief at being able to correct his misapprehension. 'To be honest, I'd completely forgotten about Jordan. And that—' her voice rippled with amusement '—must show how little I was involved.'

'Ah.' Now he was smiling with her, teeth gleaming whitely in the dark. 'I'm very glad of that. You'll never know how much.'

'Oh.' If she sounded breathless and coquettish it was because she was both. 'I'm not sure what that means.'

'It means. . .' When he trailed a finger down her cheek, she stopped breathing, did nothing to control the shiver that racked her, slid the tip of her tongue over her lips. 'It means I've been mad with jealousy since you first mentioned him.' His hand came to rest on her shoulder, one finger moving gently.

'I. . . I would never have guessed.' Hoped, yes. Dreamed, certainly.

With her heart hammering so madly against her

ribs, her brain was hardly able to filter his words; there was simply indescribable pleasure. And her reaction to that—automatic, instinctive—was to reach up, to lay her fingers against his cheekbone.

Thinking about it afterwards, Georgia decided that probably, if she had considered first, she would not have dared, so many inhibitions still lingered from her convent education, but then she would most certainly have missed out. That warm touch of firm male skin, the faintest prickle of a beard against sensitive finger pads, lungs filled with the elusive, spicy scent of him—her brain was dizzy with so many strange, delightful sensations.

And Nat's hands were linked about her waist, his mouth drifting kisses about her face, till with a sigh he gathered her close to him. 'Georgia.' Her name was uttered on a sigh of such longing, with such melting desire that all rational thought deserted her completely.

'You know...' The voice close to her cheek was ragged, and he caught at her hands which were exploring with feathery leisure all the contours of his chest. 'You know where this is going to end, don't you?'

Eyes closed, she was giving herself up, after so many years of not believing she could feel this way, to this devastating assault on her emotions. At this precious moment nothing in the world mattered. 'I know where I want it to end.' And to begin, she told herself as he swept her up into his arms and began to carry her through the hall. And then...

Then a noise, loud and insistent, intruded, forcing itself into her brain. She murmured a little protest, as a sleeper disturbed by an unpleasant dream might, then settled back into the warm cocoon of his arms, wanting never to be separated from them and... There it was again, rude and jangling.

'Damnation.' Gently he set her down on the floor, released her with an apology. 'I'm sorry, Georgia, it's a call on a special line. I must... Don't go away.'

Raking his fingers through his hair, Nat turned towards the small room he used as a den, and she followed, leaning weakly against the doorway, watching as Nat took up the mobile phone. There was no need to switch on a lamp since the room was bathed in moonlight.

'Hello? Ah, Freddy...' So, it was the Sheikh. 'Yes, I see. Well...we've been diving all day. No, you must not allow that; it would be a setback to all we've planned. If they say that then they are quite wrong. Yes, yes, I see that... Well, you know, I'm not on my own right now. You're sure that's absolutely necessary? Yes, all right, I'll be with you in half an hour.'

The receiver was replaced and Nat stood with

his back to the window, outlined against the
brilliant silver light. It was an age before he spoke,
and when he did it was with a tone of resignation.
'That was the Sheikh, as I expect you've guessed.
Come on, Georgia, we're going out.'

Her heart gave a great leap—relief that at least
she was not excluded. 'Oh?' She was afraid to say
much more, afraid she might burst into tears,
betraying the strength of her disappointment.
'Must we?' She said it coolly, as if she weren't
trembling with excitement.

'Alas,' he teased, trailing a finger down her
cheek; if he felt her shudder, he did not react. In
the half-light she caught the little twist of a smile;
his hand moved to twitch back the narrow strap
slipping from her shoulder and lingered there,
fingers hardly stroking the sensitive skin. 'Alas, *I*
must, but I promise if you come you will never
regret it, unless—' there was a change of tone, to
one more brisk and detached '—you're tired. It
has been an energetic day one way and another.'

The sudden flare in her cheeks was probably
unobserved, but she couldn't contain the slight
tremor of amusement in her voice: the idea of
fatigue when she had never in her whole life felt
more alive, more vital!

'No, I am not—*not*—in the smallest degree
tired.'

'Then come with me.'

'But where—where are we going?'

'We're going where you've always wanted to go—out into the desert. The Sheikh from time to time, and usually on impulse, organises what he calls a "picnic" for visitors. But it's unlike any picnic you've ever been to in your life. You'll come?' She nodded. 'Oh...' he paused '...you know the attitudes here. Have you anything you could put on top? While Freddy would, I know, appreciate that dress, one or two of his advisers might just think...'

'The other day I bought a kind of kaftan in the bazaar—present for my sister.'

The cheap, gauzy black cotton threaded with gold didn't look too bad, especially when she caught it about her narrow waist with a wide copper belt and the deep collar had been pulled up so that it formed an attractive frame for her face. She added some refreshing cologne for her wrists, a strong, upward sweep of liner, and took a few moments longer to check that everything was right. But then, because she couldn't bear another moment apart from Nat, she turned and almost ran from the room.

And he was in the hall waiting. He had slipped on a multicoloured waistcoat which picked up the reddish-pink of his shirt and added touches of green and gold. The slightly exotic style suited him, especially when his hair fell casually over his forehead. Her heart was behaving wildly again. She wondered if he was aware of her feelings. She had so many irrational urges—the yearning to brush the hair back from his brow, to hold her face up to his for a lingering kiss. . .

'I begin to see where the skill of designing comes in. You look pretty ravishing, and I'm beginning to think I'm mad taking you out when what I want to do more than anything in the world is stay here with you, alone. *And* to forget the rest of the world.' He lowered his head to hers, covered her mouth with his, explored with leisurely abandon till heat and passion flared between them.

'Nathan.' In her mind she had been experimenting with his name, trying to decide which version she preferred. She listened to it now as she said it in a husky voice—in a conscious imitation of a screen goddess's.

'I thought I told you—' his voice was low and intimate, causing ripples the length of her spine '—my friends call me Nat.'

'And who said—' she continued her parody, amused and excited by her own spirit, 'I had any intention of being. . .your friend?' And she allowed her mouth to brush against his.

He laughed then—a kind of growl deep in his throat, incredibly arousing. It was almost dark in the hallway, only a single lamp in a corner behind him casting a beam, but his eyes sparkled down in amused delight. 'And to think I had the idea our friendship was making distinct progress.'

'I too.' She sighed mournfully. 'But now I'm being hustled away I begin to wonder. . .'

'You're saying. . .you would much rather stay here?'

'Much.' She trailed a delicate hand down his cheek until her fingertips rested against his lips. 'Much rather.' And she was rewarded when Nat's mouth returned to hers, caressing with a gentleness which began to spiral into abandon.

'I promise. . .' he muttered against her cheek as, holding her close, he backed towards the door. 'I promise I shall remember every word later, act on it later, but. . .' reaching behind him, he managed to find the doorknob '. . .if we don't go now I swear. . .we're not going to make it. And that would be a great pity.'

He opened the door, stood aside, allowing Georgia to precede him, which, after a few fraught and breathless moments, she did.

CHAPTER SIX

USING the work vehicle—a powerful four-wheel drive—Nat negotiated the still frantic city streets, travelled down the coast road for a few miles, then switched to what was little more than a dusty track between high dunes.

Above them, the sky was of midnight-blue velvet, the moon hung low and full, white and serene, stars had been scattered with a prodigal hand. Then, quite abruptly, the track crested a ridge and the desert was revealed, stretching in endless bluffs as far as eternity.

'Stop,' cried Georgia. It was imperative to have time to absorb it all. 'Please stop for just a moment, Nat. I want to remember this as it is now, for ever.'

With the engine switched off, neither speaking, they were conscious of perfect stillness. Georgia was holding her breath, fearful of disturbing, of intruding, and—a strange sensation—it was as if her entire existence had been a prelude to this moment.

Curving parabolas of sand were highlighted and in deep shadow, sculptured, made perfect by wind and weather; nothing of man's design could show such vaulting perfection.

'Oh-h-h.' At last her breath escaped; words to express her exultation were elusive. But she reached out, twined her fingers in his.

'Mmm. It's hard to cope with, and it gets under your skin so you never quite escape. And at night, especially on a night like this, it's sheer magic.'

They drove on then, slowly, unwilling to intrude on the solitary, timeless beauty, the vehicle bucking a little as it negotiated some of the wilder contours until, quite unexpectedly, they were in a different world.

Reaching a summit, they began to drop towards an enclosed valley, green, rich with palms, here and there the glitter of water, a clutch of ancient crumbling buildings and, to one side, most striking of all, something straight out of a Hollywood epic. An enormous tent, black, topped by tiny pennants, billowed slightly in the faintest drift of wind, the flare from guttering torches spilling light through its open sides onto the sand.

Her mind dallied with the idea of Arab stallions pawing the ground, laden camels picking their way slowly, delicately along an ancient path, but when she said as much to Nat he grinned, and a moment later was pulling up alongside an assortment of off-the-road vehicles, each, judging by the state of paint and chrome, bought no later than yesterday and owing nothing to the timeless history of the place.

A wide carpet led to the entrance to the tent,

and when they reached the group inside Nathan began by introducing her to the Sheikh. Quite a tall man, impressive, with a dark beard and brilliant dark eyes which scrutinized her intently, he was dressed in white robes with ghutra and agal, the Arab headscarf and cord, but his voice and manner were entirely Oxbridge English.

'Miss Maitland, welcome to Raqat. I apologise for intruding on your evening.' She was uncertain if there was a hint of capricious amusement there, but possibly not. 'But I'm so glad you were able to come at such short notice.'

'Your Excellency—' Nat had warned her of the correct form of address '—it was kind of you to invite me.'

He bowed his head gravely. 'I hope you will have a pleasant time.'

She found that she was taken in charge of by Mina, the Sheikh's sister, considerably older than he but speaking the same perfect English, though in her case it was with a slight, deliciously liquid accent.

Georgia was introduced to a bewildering number of women, some Europeans but mostly Raqatis, many young, sloe-eyed and beautiful, one or two in traditional dress, ever ready to raise a scarf across the face, but many in western styles, though extremely decorous, with arms, necks and legs sedately covered. If she had appeared without the kaftan she would surely have felt vulgar and conspicuous, and she blessed Nat for his warning.

Over her glass of sherbet, a delicious concoction of exotic fruit juices with syrup, her eyes were constantly seeking out Nathan, and despite his being so engaged in various discussions, moving from one group of men to another, their eyes kept meeting, exchanging secret messages. Quite simply they were carrying on a clandestine flirtation, a novel experience for her and one she found stimulating and exciting.

But gradually the guests began to rearrange themselves. Georgia was persuaded onto a pile of cushions and before long felt the touch of a finger run the length of her spine. Immediately her breathing quickened, her heart leapt about inside her chest, but, determined to conceal such foolishness, she glanced casually over her shoulder and smiled.

'Surviving?' Nat's eyes were on her mouth with unmistakable intent. All her resolutions evaporated in an instant.

'More than.' There was that imitation of Marilyn Monroe again. 'And you were quite right.' She waved an expressive hand. 'It would have been a shame to miss all this.' The banal words tried to suggest an interest in the priceless Persian rugs which hung from the walls, in the huge brass salvers which flared and glinted in the flicker of the torches.

Looking up at the servant who was offering a dish of canapés, she accepted one. 'And—' she made another effort to ignore that unmistakable gleam, perhaps even to tease a little '—it might just provide the inspiration I need, help to give my career the kick-start it lacks. That, after all—' the wide green eyes were studiously innocent '—was why I came.'

'Of course it was.' He was playing the game too. 'That was exactly what I had in mind when I took you diving, and when I brought you out here this evening. And I have lots of other ideas which I'm sure will provide all the inspiration you will ever need.' From the platter of titbits left on a low table beside them he chose one, and placed it delicately between her slightly open lips.

It was a melt-in-the-mouth sort of pastry, with a mix of elusive spicy flavours. She swallowed and ran the tip of her tongue over her lips. 'You. . .' Georgia's voice was unsteady and she had no idea what she was about to say, then she said, 'You cleared up the problem with the Sheikh?'

He grinned then, his expression telling her how clearly he could read her confusion, but strangely she didn't mind, and at least he answered as if her query had been considered. 'It wasn't a real problem; he merely wanted my backing for a decision we had reached some time ago. Someone had wanted to go off at a tangent. There were other suggestions too, which had all been discarded, but it's all safely back on course.'

'Is he a marine biologist himself?' She looked across to where their host was continuing an animated discussion with a group of men, and where his sister was making her own positive contribution. Mina's total lack of inhibition surprised Georgia.

'No, he's a Maths graduate. But Mina read chemical engineering and is very much on the ball. In fact, he has just appointed her to his cabinet. She's chief adviser on the development of the oil industry.'

'Good heavens, I would never have guessed.'

'So, you're prepared to admit that this isn't entirely the male-chauvinist backwater you wanted to believe it a little while ago?'

'I wouldn't say that.'

'Go on,' Nathan teased. 'Admit you made a hasty judgement. When do you think any western government will put a woman in charge of, say, technology?'

'I'm not into reading the future,' she equivocated, 'but I confess I admire her; she strikes me as a formidably clever and efficient woman. And yes, I might as well hand it to the Sheikh too; it must have taken a bit of nerve to promote her over so many men.'

'Not really. His grandmother introduced compulsory primary education for girls and his mother

used to be chief medical officer for the sheikhdom, so, you see, emancipation isn't exactly new.'

'Oh, you!' Taking up a small cushion, she struck
him lightly, then, aghast at what could easily be
considered a social gaffe, she looked around
nervously. But fortunately attention was diverted
by the arrival of a small group of musicians who
positioned themselves at the far side of a small
area of parquet flooring.

'Now it's time for the exotic dancers.' Nat
spoke in a low voice, close to her ear.

'Oh, must we stay?' By no means certain that
she was in the mood for what was more than
likely some kind of belly dancing, Georgia sighed,
fluttering her eyelashes. 'I'm so tired, Nat. Must
we wait for this?'

'I think we must.' His hand stroked gently on
her inner wrist; the eyes looking into hers had a
lazy yet elated expression which brought a throb
of excitement to her stomach, a faint blush to her
cheeks. 'But, like you, I feel tired.' The word on
his lips held the most contradictory implications.
'In any event, it ought not to last very long and I
think the dancing will be classical more than
exotic. Some of the more explicit routines are
considered unsuitable for a mixed audience.'

And so it turned out. The music on the stringed
instruments, enhanced by the anklet bells worn
by the dancers, had rhythms so endemic, so
popular and persuasive in the bazaars, that it was

easy to listen to. And the dancers' whirling speed and dexterity were hypnotic and certainly formed a fitting climax to a day unlike any that Georgia had ever experienced—one she knew she would never forget if she lived to be a hundred.

But it would be hard to deny that such a day exacted a physical toll, so by the time the dancing had finished and the musicians had collected their instruments and quietly disappeared she was exhausted, leaning back against Nat and glad of his support.

'Come on.' As soon as he could, he rose, gently pulling her to her feet. 'You ought to be home in bed.' He was looking down at her with that quizzical, amused look—the one she couldn't quite interpret; she simply knew it took her breath away.

When they had said their goodbyes, they drifted slowly back to the parking area, she holding the hand supporting her about the waist, allowing her head to droop on his shoulder. For a few moments they lingered at the oasis pool, which was fed by an unlikely brook gurgling over large pebbles, smiling foolishly at the moon apparently lying beneath the water.

It was then that Nathan turned her into him, held her face between his hands for a moment which she wanted to last for ever. 'I shall remember this night for as long as I live.' Unconsciously he was echoing her very own thoughts. 'And, I promise you, one day we shall come back on our own. I want to show you the desert in all its aspects, all its moods. I want to take you up there—' his head indicated distant peaks '—to swim with you in a hidden pool of cool, fresh water. So many things. . .' his voice grew husky '. . .so many things I want to do with you.'

His mouth touched hers; she felt the rub of his tongue across her lips—a brief, unsatisfactory contact when she was fevered with longing. . . And then he was leading her towards the car and they were bumping their way back to the road.

In the time they had been in the desert the city had calmed, and before long they had drawn up in front of Nathan's apartment block, and were skimming skywards in the lift. In spite of her impatience and excitement, Georgia felt shy, uncertain of what would happen when they closed the door, and. . . Maybe it was too late. Had the magic moment been dissipated, had he even taken at face value her protestations of fatigue?

In the event, she behaved with amazing normality, disentangling herself from the folds of the kaftan with a sigh of relief.

'That served its purpose.' She rolled it into a ball. 'But I'd better find something else to take to Penny. I'm not sure a farmer's wife in deepest Wales would find much use for one.'

'You ought to keep it as a memento of a rather special night.' For a moment Nat stood there, hands on his hips, watching her, then he came forward, took the bundle from her hands and placed it on a chair. 'As for Penny—' now his hands were about her waist and he was looking down with an intensity which was unnerving '—it might be an idea to try some of the silver merchants; they offer very attractive jewellery and. . .'

And then, with a groan which could have given voice to her own frustrations, he pulled her into the curve of his body, burying his face in the cloud of her hair which the journey had tangled about her face. 'Tell me, Georgia.' His voice was muffled, aroused and wildly arousing. 'What were we doing wasting so much time when we might have been. . .alone together?' Then he raised his head, looked down at her, eyes sparkling with amused frustration.

'You're asking *me*?' Head tilted back, Georgia brushed her mouth softly against his—such a simple action, such turbulent pleasure. 'If you recall, I was against it from the start.' The hands which had been linked about his neck now slipped inside the open neckline of his shirt. 'But my wishes. . .'

Beneath her fingertips she could pick up the tumult of his pulses, almost as frantic as her own. As her fingers moved across the contours of his body, she felt him draw in a sudden breath. He caught at her hands.

'Are you saying. . .you're sorry we went to the

desert? Sorry we had an experience that will be with us for ever?'

'I'm not saying anything except. . .except it wasn't my idea, and if it had been my choice three hours ago. . .'

'So, you want to take up from where we left off three hours ago, when you have been telling me how tired you are?'

'Do I have to spell it out for you?'

But she didn't, for he swept her up into his arms, carrying her into that room of the apartment which she had previously avoided.

Then they were standing together in a bedroom which some part of her mind recorded as much like her own—two large beds, fine curtaining which stirred in a breath of wind, patterned by moonlight. And his arm was still possessively hooked about her waist so her feet didn't quite touch the floor. 'You're sure?' His mouth feathered kisses down her cheek, halted against hers.

'Very, very sure.' Hearts were beating in tempestuous unison, and in a strange way Georgia was detached, intrigued by her rapidly acquired expertise in this game, this way she had of allowing her lips to part encouragingly, in quite blatant invitation.

But all the theorising was swept aside as her emotions moved into top gear, her body overwhelmed with spiralling pleasure.

Nat's mouth moved on; she lay back against his arms, allowing him easy access to her throat. . .

'For heaven's sake.' It was a despairing groan, now only half-amused. 'Tell me how this dress fastens, or, more to the point in these circumstances, how it unfastens.'

'Just here.' One smooth, shameless move pulled down the zip. His hands brushed against the delicate straps and she gave a tiny wriggle and felt the dress slip from her body, land in a pool of silk on the floor.

Shame, perplexity, embarrassment, guilt—all these she ought to have been feeling. But instead there was what? Impatience? Yes, a great deal of that as she fumbled with buttons. Relief when she pushed the shirt from his shoulders. Indescribable joy and pleasure as her hands moved unrestricted across his chest. Intoxication as she lowered her face to the silky skin. . .

'Do you know—' he caught at her fingers, took them one at a time to his mouth, kissed each open palm lingeringly '—have you the least idea what you're doing to me?'

'I hope. . .' She shook her head in disbelief, felt the hair bell out about her face, loved the exultation in Nat's eyes as he followed its hazy, gleaming movement. 'Very much I hope it's doing to you—' she gave a delicious shudder as his fingers delicately outlined the full curve of her breast '—just what you. . .what you are. . .doing to me.'

'You must know it.' Gently he pushed her onto the bed and a moment later joined her, lying apart from her at first, only his mouth in tantalising contact, an occasional trailing touch the length of her spine, that oh, so delicate hand on her breast taking her to a fever pitch of awareness and impatience.

'You know—' his lips moved against hers '—this is where I've been longing to be since that first day when I saw you downstairs in the hallway.'

'I don't believe you.' She breathed the words into his mouth. 'You showed no sign.'

'If you had been prepared to look, you would have seen it.'

'But didn't you promise me. . .? Ah-h-h.' It was a gasp of pleasure.

'What?' He made a trail of kisses across her cheek. 'What did I promise?'

'You said no strings—' a tiny giggle '—and guess what.'

'What?'

'I really thought you meant it.'

'I did.' But then Nat turned her onto her back, pinning her arms above her head on the pillows, and began a leisurely exploration of her body, introducing her to sensations that she hadn't believed in. Who could have imagined that such a touch, such a feathery, delicate touch, could be so drugging, so intoxicating?

Nothing she had ever dreamed had made her imagine this bewildering mix—such touching, such tasting and feeling. One of her hands was released, was freed to circle his neck, fingers reaching down to explore slowly, slowly the silky warmth of his back. And then she felt such an explosion of feeling that she arched against him, felt his arms sweep around her, supporting, colluding and her eagerness and... Dear Lord she thought she would never...

'Georgia. Georgia.' With increased fervour he was drifting kisses the length of her throat, between her breasts.

'Nathan.' She held his mouth against her skin, would have imprisoned it there for ever. 'I can't believe... I didn't know...didn't dream it could ever be like this...'

'I promise you...' He raised his head, flicking the thick dark hair from his eyes. 'I promise you...' The dominant figure loomed over her. 'I promise you, Georgia...' The voice drifted away as slowly, with expert tender passion, he began to fulfil all those wild, impetuous promises that lovers had been making to each other since the beginning of time.

CHAPTER SEVEN

THE room, when Georgia woke, was softly bright with filtered sunshine. She lay still, her eyes moving lazily, absorbing familiar yet unfamiliar detail. Beside her, very close to the bed, spread carefully over a blue, silk-covered armchair was her dress with—here she gave a little shamed giggle, felt a faint warmth in her skin—just peeping out, the only other garment she had worn beneath her dress—a tiny scrap of skin-coloured lace.

For a few moments her mind remained deliciously hazy; only, she knew hers had not been the hands dealing with her things so neatly. Something had happened—something so deliciously mind-blowing that. . .

And in an instant her mind was alive with a bewildering recollection of sublime experiences. She sighed, her eyes drifted closed, a smile curved her mouth and she turned on her side, hands reaching out for the pillow where Nat's head had rested. She cradled it into her body, making believe that he was with her still. But of course she knew that she was alone in the flat. Vaguely she remembered how she had woken earlier and he had leaned across to touch his mouth to hers. 'I must go.'

'No.' Persuasively she had spread her fingers delicately across his chest—so quickly she had discovered what was arousing for both of them. 'Please, Nat, please.' She had pouted, flirted outrageously. 'Not yet. Not just yet.'

His groan had been one of surrender, sheer delight—proof, if she'd needed it, of her newly acquired power. And yet, as he'd raised himself on one elbow, looming over her, smiling, brushing tendrils of hair from her forehead, dropping tiny kisses on her closing eyelids, she'd known with that potent, lurching joy that there was nothing one-sided about that power, that she was victim as much as he; they were both such free and willing victims.

Mouths had been for the moment their only contact. It had been very nearly chaste, certainly tantalising, teasing, giving and taking. Then, with a deep shudder of regret, impatience, submission—she didn't know which—he'd settled above her. She'd linked her arms about his neck, drawing him down so that she'd felt the brush of his skin against hers, given herself wholly to this new delight, the bewitching delight of his expert lovemaking, abandoned herself to the joy of it.

Inevitably, now, it was late. She lay for a while dreaming, stretching idly, dazed with happiness which even when she had showered seemed in no

way inclined to diminish. Each time she passed a
mirror a glance would reveal that secret smile,
that glow of newly acquired happiness which was
so unmistakable, so transforming.

'I shall be back as soon as I can make it,' Nat
had whispered against her cheek, leaning over her
in the half-dark, unwilling to disturb her.

The scent of him still lingered in Georgia's
nostrils. His skin cool from his shower, his face
smooth and with the elusive tang of that spicy
cologne. It had been hard to resist setting out on
that whole seductive process again, especially
when he'd murmured, 'I don't know how I'm
going to exist without you.' But then, doubtless
sensing danger, he had gone swiftly, and when
she had heard the soft clunk of the outer door
closing she had quite simply transferred him to
her dreams.

And in a way it was good to have the apartment
to herself, to have time to consider what had
happened, to think of the future and the implications... Certainly it was a relief that Ismail and
Enna were still on leave, otherwise slopping about
half-dressed would have been impossible.

A diversion just after midday took her away
from the salad that she was preparing for her
lunch. The doorbell brought a momentary surge
of hope that Nat had for some reason cancelled
his trip, which was, of course, ridiculous. Besides,
he had his own doorkey, but it was an anticlimax

to open the door and find a local messenger standing there. But he was carrying, under a cover of shiny Cellophane, a sheaf of the most perfect roses that she had ever seen.

When she had scribbled her name on the receipt, returned it and leaned back against the now closed door, she saw the tiny envelope nestling among the foliage; her lips curved in a smile as she slid a finger beneath the flap. She read:

Darling Georgia,
   Thank you for last night. I shall be with you sooner than I dared hope. In the meantime, go out and buy the most stunning dress you can find. I have something special to ask you.
   N.

Her mind went blank for just a moment before her imagination raced into overdrive. Right back at the beginning hadn't he told her he had a proposition...? She still couldn't recall if he had said proposition or proposal. Singing lightly beneath her breath, she went to slip on some clothes. If he wanted her to buy a special dress, then this time surely it could mean just one thing...?

She gave herself a smug glance as she passed a mirror. And if he wanted her to wear something stunning then she had seen the very thing the other day—admittedly in one of Raqat's most exclusive boutiques, where a simple scarf cost the earth, but, what the heck, she would use her credit card. After all, when a man like Nathan Trehearn gave you such instructions, then you jumped.

Still smiling, rather inanely now, she decided, failing in her attempt to look more seriously amused, Georgia did consider whether she might be falling into the age-old trap of allowing a man to call the tune while she danced. Possibly, she told herself with sickening self-satisfaction, but what choice had she, since it was the one thing in the world she wanted to do?

Returning to the apartment in the early evening, Georgia dropped her packages with a weary sigh, made her way to the kitchen and set about making a pot of tea. Minutes later she was lying on the balcony, draining a first cup of the life-giving liquid and about to reach out to the pot for a refill, when she was disturbed by the insistent ringing of a telephone—not the usual one which stood silently on the hall table, but Nat's special line, which she traced to his study.

'Hello?' Knowing that it was his direct contact with the Sheikh's advisers, she wasn't surprised by the background gabble of Arabic before a female voice asked in English, 'Miss Maitland?'

'Speaking.'

'One moment, please; Mr Trehearn wishes to speak with you.'

'Georgia.' No one else ever spoke her name with that particular intonation, and the air of intimacy brought on a feeling of shyness and. . . something else. It made her feel. . .cherished.

'Nathan.' The breathy voice again, the teenager overwhelmed at being noticed by her favourite pop idol. 'Nathan, thank you for the gorgeous, wonderful roses.'

'Ah, they came. They ought to have been red but I couldn't resist the cream ones. So cool and. . .serene, rather like you.'

'Cool?' Now she was teasing, more in charge. 'Serene? What have I done to make you think I'm either of those?'

'Ah, but, you see, I'm in the privileged position of knowing the truth about you. So long as you continue to appear so—'

'Nathan!' It was a reproof to conceal the excited bounding of her heart.

'Yes?' Laughter in his voice. 'I'm here.'

'Nothing,' she confessed. 'Just Nathan. But I thought you were supposed to be in Switzerland?'

'I am in Switzerland—simply calling through the Raqat office. And now for the good news! I'll be back tomorrow.'

'Tomorrow?' It was earlier than Georgia had dared to hope.

'You sound. . .pleased?'

'What do you think?'

'I think I got it right. And have you had the chance to go and buy that dress as I suggested?'

'Oh, it was a *suggestion*? I took it more as a command!'

'Ah, right. I'm glad you got the message.'

'And I bought something. It's—'

'*Don't* tell me,' he interrupted swiftly, then added mysteriously, 'It might be unlucky. But I'll be back about nine tomorrow night. Be ready then. Timing is all-important. Be ready to be whisked away for a very special occasion.'

'Oh, you must tell me; I can't stand—'

'No questions. It's all going to be a surprise.'

'A pleasant one, I hope?'

'That, I think, I can promise. But now I must go. . .'

'Oh. . .must you?'

'Truly I must. Sleep well, Georgia.'

'I shan't. Not without you. Goodnight, Nathan.' And as she replaced the receiver she whispered, 'I love you.' It was the first time either of them had made that declaration. So simple, so very basic, it had been overtaken by a hundred more extravagant statements. Especially in the sweet torment of lovemaking, when more showy protestations were the norm.

But doubtless, like her, he was waiting for the right moment. Certainly it was difficult over the telephone, with the possibility of all kinds of eavesdroppers. In any event. . .her mind was a miasma of sheer pleasure...what construction could anyone put on the plans he had outlined except that he meant to propose marriage, no less? Anything else would be too much of an anticlimax and in her mind she was totally secure as to what her answer would be.

Only, by eight the next evening, she was a quivering mass of nerves and uncertainty. Suppose she had picked up entirely the wrong signs? Nat might be about to propose oh...anything rather than marriage. A holiday in the West Indies was just one of the ideas which occurred to her.

There was little doubt that she was overwrought, in spite of having spent the greater part of the day in a series of supposedly relaxing pursuits. Sheer self-indulgence most of them had been, and hideously expensive, at Raqat's opulent health and beauty salon.

A Turkish bath had come first, followed by a long, soothing massage with sweet oils and unguents, intent on smoothing away every sign of tension. Then her hair had been given a glowing rinse to enhance the old-gold sheen and a style a little more bouffant than normal but which seemed to balance her high cheekbones. A manicure had left her hands looking more slender and graceful than ever.

It was time at last to slip the dress over her head, which she did with great care for the delicate, silky material. Watching as, after a twitch, it settled on her shoulders as if it had been made for her.

The pale cream chiffon was caught beneath the bust and fell in delicate folds to just above the ankle. With a perfectly plain, round neckline and small puff sleeves at the front, it was only at the back—she had to adjust mirrors to enjoy the full effect—that it plunged to a deep, dramatic V. Acres of peachy, sun-kissed skin were criss-crossed by narrow ribbons. And, to be worn with it, there was a huge, enveloping square of matching filmy material, very adaptable and practical in a country where too much bare female skin was considered immodest.

Experimenting, she threw it over her shoulders and arranged it over her head and face, Arab-style, so only the startling green eyes could be seen—gleaming in self-mockery. She thought—no, she *knew* that Nathan was going to approve.

The sound of a key in the lock caused her to swirl the scarf away from her, took her skimming into the hall, where she was in time to see the door open; she saw him stand there for a moment, then, pushing the door closed, he came towards her—slowly, one hand behind his back, absorbing every detail of her appearance while she. . .

Well, she was doing exactly the same to him, to this man who—one would never have believed it possible—was looking more like her idea of male perfection than ever. He was smiling at her. Just. His lips were turning slightly up at the corners and. . .and she was mad for him, longing for him to pull her impatiently into the bedroom, which might be a pity—her mind split on this thought— when he looked so indescribably gorgeous.

He wore a pale suit—almost, now that she thought to compare, a perfect match for her dress, a shade or two darker, perhaps—and a silk shirt, a tie in subtle swirls of pink and brown and. . .and he smelt deliciously of. . .the spices of Araby; that was a flight of fancy. His hair, she could see, had been trimmed, not too short, and even now was falling over his forehead, which seemed to be its inevitable way.

Just everything about the man was sheer perfection. And he was smiling—not grinning, as she was so afraid she was—but smiling in that intimate, intense way which made her heart flip over, and he was saying something. She saw his lips move, his teeth gleam; the words—she caught them at last.

'You look. . .quite delightful.'

'And you.' She waited for him to take her in his arms, was willing, if that was his inclination, to abandon whatever glamorous outing he had arranged to. . . But. . .his hand appeared, was offering a posy. No, it was more a bouquet, of the most delicate blossoms—every shade from ivory to a deep, rich amber, nestling among a froth of pale fern.

'For. . .the bride.' Their eyes were in searching contact, a shade of anxiety in his which passed after a second.

'Oh. . .' Georgia looked from Nat to the flowers, one slender, pink-tipped finger going out to touch a rosebud the colour of gilded saffron, so beautiful that she felt a sting of tears. 'You're spoiling me ridiculously.'

'And I mean to go on doing that. For evermore.'

'Oh. . .' Something in his eyes told her that he was about to explain.

'I want you to marry me, Georgia. No—' he stopped whatever she had been about to say '—wait a moment. I mean now. . .this evening.'

'Nathan!' Any shock she might have experienced was overwhelmed by a wave of sheer pleasure. Triumph too might have lurked at the back of her mind, for always there had been a doubt that he. . . But for now there was only pleasure, intense and pure. The vague query was something to be swept aside; later would be time enough to put that to him, and in any case he was saying something about it. . .

'There are reasons. Later I'll explain, but right now. . . All the arrangements have been made; transport is waiting.'

There was nothing to be considered, but she

said, 'One moment.' Burying her face in the blossoms, Georgia continued to look at him, the sparkling delight in the green eyes making all the promises that she was, at this moment, too shy to voice.

Then as she turned away he said, 'Wait.' It was a command which she obeyed with a provocative glance over her shoulder.

'Mmm?' Her mouth was soft with mischievous laughter.

'I love the dress,' he said as he laughed down at her his fingers tracing her backbone. 'But I prefer you. . .' He stepped back, white teeth gleaming. 'I shan't embarrass you by saying any more. *Not* when we're about to be married.'

Into the bedroom she hurried, reappearing a moment later decorously wrapped in the veiling, the hand holding the bouquet just peeking out. 'Is this better?'

'Everything about you is always better; I thought you knew that.' For a long moment Nat held her against him, long enough for her to realise that the strain was affecting him as much as her; then they were out of the apartment, being whisked the short distance to the landing-pad where a helicopter, with the Shekih's personal cipher emblazoned on the sides, was waiting for them.

Thereafter it was all a dream, but one she recognised. They were in the desert setting she

already knew, though this was the first time she
had approached it from the air. The draught from
the rotors made the tent billow before they settled
down on the sand. Above them was the same
moon, white and gleaming, the same extravagance
of stars. . .

But this time the tent gave a different
impression. There were no guests except for the
Sheikh and his sister and, where before the walls
had been draped with dark colours, now they
were lighter, with pale silk hangings richly
embroidered with exotic birds and flowers.

Together they walked up the central carpet as
the Sheikh came forward to greet them, Georgia
and Nathan putting their hands together in the
traditional gesture of respect. As usual the Sheikh
was wearing the familiar robes, but this time had
his head uncovered, which seemed to make him
look a little younger.

At his side was his sister, who took Georgia
into a little recess where they tried out various
styles with the chiffon scarf till Mina found one
she considered suitable, then they went back to
where Nathan and the Sheikh were waiting. It
was startling to see that Nathan too was now
wearing Arab robes, though it should hardly have
been surprising since Nathan had told her how
close his friendship with Freddy was—they were
almost blood brothers, apparently. And there was

no doubt that he looked particularly handsome and romantic in his desert gear.

But now the Sheikh was talking, standing in front of them, Mina to one side. And there was a sudden formality about the situation which made Georgia reach out in sudden nervousness for Nathan's hand. And since the ceremony was conducted in Arabic she had no idea what was being said, until Freddy switched to English at the end.

'And now, by virtue of my position, I declare you to be married according to the laws of Raqat. I wish you great joy.' He leaned forward, kissing Georgia briefly, embracing Nathan warmly. 'May you have many sons.' There were more kisses and good wishes from Mina and then Freddy said, 'Now we must go, Nathan. I know you will excuse us.' Here the Sheikh grinned at his own joke. 'I *may* see you tomorrow, if you can spare the time.'

There was another flash of white teeth, and a moment or two later there was the sound of powerful engines as the helicopter prepared for lift off. Watching the huge machine, Georgia felt that she must wake up soon.

But an arm about her waist was all the assurance she needed. 'Shall we have a walk to the pool?' Nat asked. And they did, not speaking till they reached the little oasis.

They watched the water fall into the pool and saw the same old moon lying on the pebbles, then he was turning her towards him. 'I can hardly believe this is happening.' His mouth was on hers, coaxing her lips to part for him.

'It isn't. Only. . .it doesn't matter in the least.'

'Shall we go back? I think they're fixing us a special supper. Not—' he paused, his cheek against hers '—that I'm the least bit hungry.'

'But I am.' It was diverting to be so positively contradictory, 'I am simply starving.'

They had reached the long carpet, and before going inside he turned her towards him again. 'So much for romance. I lay all this on for you.' He waved a hand, directing her amused attention to the entire sweep of the desert: sky, stars more profuse, or so it seemed, then the grains of sand beneath their feet, the full white moon, all the sand, windswept into fantastic sculptures—all the artefacts of nature which might have been designed to illustrate man's puny insignificance. 'And all you can say is that you are starving.'

When he had spoken, Nat shrugged the cream cotton robes from his shoulders, handing them to a servant who had appeared from the shadows; now he gently unwrapped the scarf from Georgia's head.

'I'm sorry.' This was a game she didn't mind playing. 'Don't imagine I'm not grateful, and wildly impressed. I can think of nothing more wonderful than. . .all this. It proves how very influential you are.'

'Thank you.' His expression was droll. 'But, Georgia, my darling, you are starving, and since I've made all kinds of promises. . .'

'Ah, yes, you must tell me what all this was about; it is a great disadvantage not knowing.'

'I had to put your well-being at the very top of my list.'

'Good.'

'Along with my camels and hunting dogs.'

'Really?'

'And truly.' The expression on her face caused him to laugh aloud, and they were still laughing when the servant approached again, deferentially addressing Nathan while his speculative eyes scrutinised Georgia.

A few incomprehensible words, a reply from Nathan and they were ushered into one of the rooms behind the main reception area, where a small round table was set with two places. Georgia sat in the chair which was being offered to her, watching while Nathan, after a brief conversation with the servant, took the place opposite.

It was hard not to be impressed by the grandeur of the room. The walls were hung with Persian carpets, the deep, rich shades enhanced by the flicker of shaded candles. There were tables with beaten brass ornaments, divans straight out of the *Arabian Nights*, strewn with silk cushions and fringed shawls.

Silently the servant brought the food—slices of

cool fruits to begin and some kind of fruity, spicy chicken dish for the main course.

'Mmm.' Georgia approved the subtly piquant flavour. 'This is simply delicious.'

'Well, I did ask Freddy to provide something fairly bland. I didn't want you to suffer any more tummy upsets.'

It was a moment before she remembered, and when she did she determined not to laugh. 'How very romantic of you to remind me.' But it was impossible to stop her lips curving into a grin.

'Don't be provocative. It isn't seemly in a young woman so very recently married.'

'Well, I have no intention of conforming to some stereotype.'

'You do realise don't you. . .?' Here he paused while the servant poured wine into glasses. They exchanged a few words and the man left silently. 'You do realise that when Saad and the cook go off on their new Yamaha sand vehicles, you and I will be alone with no other human life for many miles. . .for hundreds of miles in some directions? Then you might think it more circumspect to try to please your husband as you promised just a little while ago.'

'I was taken advantage of, didn't know what I was doing. In fact, I don't think I was asked to make any promises.'

'Ah, but that is how things work here. The questions were posed, your silence was taken for acceptance, and more than likely Freddy is congratulating himself on having found for me a compliant and submissive wife.'

'I didn't know he had found me for you.' Eyes wide, Georgia stared at Nat across the table.

'No?' The dark eyebrows arched; pleasure and delight were clearly etched on his features.

'No, I truly thought it was the other way round—that he had found you for me.'

'Whatever.' His hand came across and covered hers. 'Whatever. Fate brought us together. I shall be eternally grateful.' Then he reached out for his glass, raised it. 'To us, Georgia.' The light-hearted teasing had given way, was replaced by an air of intense and private joy. 'And to this perfect moment.'

'To you, Nathan. To you for making me so happy.'

'And this,' he promised, rising in his chair so that he could lean across and touch his mouth to hers, 'is only the beginning.'

CHAPTER EIGHT

THE next weeks passed in a blur of pleasure—a dream from which Georgia occasionally and briefly awoke to marvel at herself for taking to domestic life with such instant and abandoned enthusiasm. Never had she judged herself so ready to 'settle down', though that term was totally in conflict with the emotional ferment of her present condition.

Of course, deep down she occasionally assured herself that what she was experiencing was not exactly typical of domestic life. Hers was on a different plane, altogether more exotic, more exciting and glamorous, and besides, there weren't many men like Nathan. And what was so wonderful was that Nat felt the same way she did—regretting the hours they had to spend apart, sometimes arranging for her to accompany him when he had to do some work in the field.

There was the magical day when, as he had promised back at the beginning, he took her further along the coast to a deeper part of the reef, where it was more mysterious and dim, with still more strange, outlandish sea creatures, some as curious as they were. With anyone else she would have been nervous, but with Nat never more than a yard from her side she was totally confident, glowing with pride when he remarked on the fact.

'You're going to be a great asset,' Nat teased when they were back on board and he was watching her rub at her sodden hair with a towel.

'I wondered why you had married me.' Tossing the towel aside, Georgia reached for the basket of food that Enna had provided.

'Mmm. That was why.' Grey eyes sparkled down into green. 'I wanted. . .quite desperately I wanted. . .someone who would be good at taking notes among—'

'Ah? Then that lets me out. I never could pick up shorthand.'

'Among other things, I was about to say.' The expression on his face was one which she was beginning to recognise—one which drove away all inclination for food and made her aware of the blood circulating in her veins.

'Other things?' The tip of a pink tongue slid across her upper lip. 'And what. . .exactly. . .are those other things you had in mind?'

'Come inside.' He was smiling, persuasive. 'Then I might be prepared to. . .to discuss those other things at some length.'

'Oh, Nathan, no.' She caught at the hand in the act of pushing aside her bra strap. 'No! We mustn't; someone might—'

'You said that before. In the desert.' Now his eyes had that lazy, seductive gleam which made her breathless; her lips parted to ease the feverish excitement. 'Remember?' And when she gave one quick nod, Nat's mouth curved in satisfaction. 'And when I told you we were the only humans for miles?' Again an eager nod. 'And was I right?'

'Yes. Yes, you were.'

'Well. . .' His arm came about her waist. *Her* hand was flat against his skin; she could feel the heat from his body as he pulled her to him. She was uncertain if the throb in her ears was her own heartbeat or his. But one thing she knew was that, whatever he wanted, she would be more than willing. 'Was I right and—' now his mouth was moving against hers '—did we have three days of the most marvellous and. . .relaxing—?'

'Exhausting, I would have said.'

His laugh was a deep reverberation in his chest. 'You sound *exhausted* now. So come inside, where it is cool and shadowy and where we can. . .discuss the matter more fully.' Which she did, of course.

And then there was the occasion, when they were persuaded to attend a ball at the club and where, once she had overcome her initial reluctance, Georgia found herself glorying in the role of. . . well, she could just about imagine the kind of tittle-tattle which was going on in the background.

She had chosen to wear a long, flowing skirt in

shades of sea-green, with here and there splashes of poppy-red, and a filmy white blouse with a stand-up collar framing a face which glowed with happiness. And which had numbers of unattached males almost begging for her attention.

'You're to accept no more invitations.' Her hand was cradled in Nat's, his mouth moved against her hair and he held her close as they moved in time to some old-fashioned music.

'Why?' She was beginning to feel sleepy. 'Why is that?' Her finger moved idly at the nape of his neck.

'Because I'm wildly jealous if you must know.' His arm tightened threateningly.

'Mmm.' She appeared to consider. 'And how do you think I feel when I see you dancing cheek-to-cheek with Melanie Jacobs?'

Cheek-to-cheek?' he scoffed indignantly, pulling away from her and glaring down. 'How you exaggerate. Besides, I told you, she's a friend of the family.'

'Perhaps all the more reason for me to feel jealous,' she said seriously, knowing she felt no such thing. 'Anyway, I forbid you to dance with her again.' Then on a sudden thought she added, 'Did you tell her about us?'

'No, of course not. Didn't we agree to say nothing until we had gone back to England and spoken to your father?'

'I simply wondered, since she's such a *close* friend.'

'I didn't say that.' Looking down, Nat shook his head reprovingly. 'I did not say *close*. Anyway, as it happened, Melanie did ask some leading questions which I did my best to field, and. . . Why are you laughing?' It was a silly question, since by this time he was laughing too. 'You enjoy being provocative, don't you?'

'And you hate it?' she was all wide-eyed innocence now.

'It's just one of the reasons I'm so crazy about you.'

Life returned to something approaching the mundane when, being obliged to chair a series of conferences involving the states with direct interest in the Red Sea environment, Nathan set off on a trip which would take him to Cairo, Amman and Riyadh.

Being without him was so painful that Georgia could cope only by keeping herself as busy as possible. She picked up her sketch-pad, which had been neglected, and with Ismail to drive her was able to visit some of the more remote parts of the city—places where she could observe without being easily observed, could put down on paper a kaleidoscope of impressions without giving offence, and this way could profitably—at least so she thought—fill in the first few days.

And if she did lie at night tossing and turning in the dark, desperate for the touch of Nat's skin on hers, then, quite simply, that was the price one had to pay for the exquisite agony of being in love. There was no shadow in her mind, no premonition that her marriage was about to shatter as precipitately as it had begun. And much, much more traumatically.

It had begun as an ordinary sort of day, except, of course, that Nathan was due back in twenty-four hours. Enna and Ismail had had time off and were not due back until the evening, and Georgia was enjoying having the house to herself. An hour was spent tidying her drawings. There were one or two of Enna which she laid to one side, meaning to give her later. And the others...? Well, she had a little dream that one day...one day she might take up her career again and would incorporate them...

And there was the doorbell! This time she did not even consider that it might be Nathan. After all, when he had called her last night he hadn't said he'd be back early. And besides, he always carried his own door key. Swiftly she thrust everything back inside the folder and went through to the hall.

When she opened the door Georgia found herself almost pushed to one side when a woman thrust impatiently past her, followed by a porter who was instructed to put a considerable number of cases 'over in the corner'.

'I beg your pardon?' Blind panic was Georgia's first reaction. She had no idea how to deal with this sudden and confident intrusion. 'I've no idea what you're doing here but I think you must have made a mistake. This flat belongs to—'

'That will be all. Thank you.' The porter was dismissed with a few coins before the woman turned her attention on Georgia. 'And thank you, honey.' She had a strong Southern accent, a sarcastic manner, and wore huge dark sunglasses, which now were pushed to the top of her very blonde head. 'But I'm perfectly aware who owns the apartment.'

About thirty, Georgia decided, the woman was casually but very expensively dressed in designer gear—blue jeans just a shade too tight and a baby-blue silk shirt which was a perfect match for her eyes. There was a cold calculation in the way she took in every detail of Georgia's appearance, making her regret her choice of sports top and shorts. 'But more to the point,' the confident voice went on, 'who are you and what are you doing in *our* apartment?'

'Your. . .' There was an implication here that she didn't understand, didn't even want to understand, and Georgia couldn't continue.

'Isn't Nat here?'

'N-no. But. . .who are you?'

'I'm Marylou.' She actually smiled then, though one would have sworn that amusement was not one of her regular emotions. 'Isn't it strange that so many men forget to mention these things? Didn't he mention he had a wife, honey?'

Of course she knew—no one knew better than she—that it was a point men sometimes forgot to mention...but Nathan? Pain stabbed at her heart, a mist came down over her eyes and her brain was in a spin, and then...the sound of another name being spoken intruded—one she tried to latch onto. 'Philippa? Was that what you just said? Philippa or—?'

'Yes—' the woman sounded as if she was losing patience '—my daughter—who keeps asking when her father is coming home. Kids do miss their parents. I don't suppose that ever occurs to...' she sent Georgia a slow, patronising glance which fortunately Georgia was too shocked to notice '...to people like you.' It was obvious where she was laying the entire responsibility for her child's loss. Then she said, 'Where is Ismail? I need some help with my bags.'

'Oh...' Her legs having refused to hold her any longer, Georgia slumped into a chair. She looked up, dazed. 'Oh, I gave them some time off. They'll be back later this evening.'

Irritation was in every line of her body as Marylou tapped her way across the marble floor to where her bags had been piled. 'Well, perhaps you. . .' She turned back to Georgia. 'Miss. . .?'

'Maitland. Georgia Maitland.'

'Well, perhaps you can lend a hand.'

On autopilot, Georgia rose, picked up two of the smaller bags and followed the American woman along the corridor, too numb to register relief when they passed the door of the room she had shared with Nathan, going instead into the one at the far end of the corridor. And it was because her face was so firmly averted that she missed the quick, sardonic glance that was flashed in her direction before the woman dropped her cases onto the floor.

'Now, I'm simply dying for a cold drink.' She led the way back towards the kitchen, picked up a can from the fridge, pulled the tab and raised it to her lips. 'And perhaps you can explain exactly what you're doing here. And—' she wiped her mouth with a tissue pulled from the box on the window-sill '—maybe even tell me when we might expect to see Nathan back.'

The effort to act with a degree of normality was almost superhuman but Georgia made it, trying to overcome the frozen mask of her face, to find words that made some sense. 'As to that, I'm not sure. From what I gather, he had some important meetings to attend. In fact. . .' Tears stung so suddenly at her eyes that she was unable to continue for a moment. She had reached out for a tissue before pride returned, made her hand drop to her side. 'In fact—' her voice barely trembled '—I'm not in your husband's confidence—' that, at least, was all too bleakly true '—and I really have no idea when he'll be back.'

'Oh, well, there's nothing new in that.' Marylou tossed her empty can in the direction of the bin, not noticing that it missed. 'Nat always has been highly secretive about his comings and goings. Which is why I feel so curious about your presence here, Miss... Maitland. You see, he is usually so discreet.'

Numb with misery, Georgia stared back at the woman, uncaring that she would be easily able to diagnose her state of mind. It was all so obvious. Nathan's wife was letting her know that she was just one in a line, that her husband was a womaniser, something she accepted as many another wife was obliged to do.

'Now I must make some calls.' Georgia had the distinct feeling that she was being dismissed. Marylou passed her, going straight to the telephone in the hall and ringing a number. A moment later she said, 'Hi, Melanie. Yeah, a good flight.' Georgia hurried past in the direction of the bedroom, but she couldn't help overhearing the next few words. 'No, Philippa is at home with her grandparents, but I've promised her...'

Melanie. That could be only one person— Melanie Jacobs, the friend of the family. Of course. As Georgia's brain whirled round in fevered circles she was putting things together. What he had failed to say was 'a friend of my wife'. Naturally that would have been putting the cat among the pigeons with a vengeance.

'Well?' Suddenly Marylou appeared in the doorway. 'Are you going to explain why you happen to be sharing Nathan's flat? As I said, the scenario is not the usual one.'

No? Georgia, who longed to know what *was* the usual scenario but would not humble herself by asking, raised her chin and looked directly at her tormentor, and embarked on the slightly incoherent tale of the mix-up over the downstairs flat. 'I'm sure Pete will confirm if you ask him.'

'Oh, I'm sure.' Marylou's voice dripped sarcasm. 'And, of course, Nat was on hand with an irresistible offer.'

'Yes.' Georgia began to stuff clothes into her cases, which had been stored in an empty cupboard. 'It was so kind of him.'

'Ah, yes. He is a very kind man. Especially where young women are concerned.' Marylou took time to light a cigarette, blowing the smoke impatiently away from her, surveying Georgia in silence. 'And are you going to tell me, Miss Maitland—' she spoke as if she found something intrinsically humorous about the name '—that you and Nat haven't been sleeping together?'

Georgia raised her head, looking blindly for a

moment at this woman whom Nathan had married, then spoke quietly. 'I think it best, don't you, if I leave at once? So, if you don't mind...' Zipping closed one of her bags, she edged into the corridor and then into the hall.

'Since you put it like that then I can only say I'm pleased you're acting so reasonably. I don't enjoy these scenes, you know,' said Marylou, implying that she had participated in a great many of them.

Two hours later, Georgia was sitting in the airport lounge waiting for her London flight to be called. Of the trip by taxi from the flat she had no recollection. She had simply found herself dumped here with not the vaguest idea of how she had arrived.

Her only thought was of escape. Or rather it was more of a desire, a need to find some secret lair where she could hide herself away, lick her wounds, nurse herself back to some kind of life—assuming that to be a remote possibility. And the only place that suggested itself was her own flat in London. There she could bolt the door, draw down the blinds and weep—weep till she had eased some of the misery out of her system.

And, in one respect at least, luck seemed to be on her side. She'd arrived at the booking desk just as the clerk had been on the telephone taking details of a cancellation on a flight to Heathrow, and thus her immediate problem had been solved. The thought of being forced to seek out overnight accommodation... She didn't think she would have been able to summon the energy. It was just a relief to be rid of her cases, to sit down in the corner of the lounge and to know that pretty soon she would be on her way.

Meanwhile, her energies were concentrated on trying to blot from her mind all that had happened. She wished, with intense desperation, that she had never heard of Raqat, much less visited it.

Around her, all the business of the airport continued. Planes disgorged their loads and families met and parted, with all the small dramas that such occasions involved. The flowing robes reminded her so strongly of...of that film of Lawrence... Desperately she tried to latch her mind onto that, but a different picture *would* intrude...

But no, she refused to allow it. Quite savagely she got to her feet and walked across to the far side of the hall. In a glass she saw the tall woman in pale chinos and jade silk shirt, slender but shapely, with wheat-coloured hair—she had been given no time to do anything with it, so it swayed about a face that was wan and colourless... Distressed by what she saw, she turned to walk back then stopped abruptly, panic overwhelming her.

On the far side of the concourse was a group of men—five or six locals and two westerners, and one of those, the tallest of the group by half a head, was the last man she had expected to see. For a few seconds it was easy to indulge herself by looking. He was talking with such verve and confidence—both hands were used in a chopping movement as he illustrated some point—and the men all laughed.

The pain above Georgia's heart was excruciating, but at the same time there was a perverse pleasure in recognising the dynamic presence of the man. Nat was so totally relaxed, in such control. And handsome. Oh, yes, she could recognise that now. How bitter it was to admit at this stage that he was everything she had ever dreamed of finding in a man—everything and more. . .

A sob rose in her throat, threatening to choke her. . . And at that precise moment Nat raised his head and, still laughing, he stared directly across at her.

Instinct made her withdraw into the shadow of a pillar, where she froze for a second, hoping to escape detection, but she saw the smile fade from his face, saw it replaced by a puzzled expression. He said a word to his friends, raised an apologetic hand, then was crossing the almost empty expanse, rapidly closing the distance between them.

Then she too began to move, knowing that if she could reach the powder room she would be safe till her flight was called. Sensing him gaining on her, she lengthened her stride, but. . .

'Georgia.' A few more yards and she might have made it, but just then a whole family—parents, grandparents, children, servants—suddenly pushed a convoy of trolleys in front of her, cutting off her escape route.

'Georgia.' His hand was on her arm, with the touch that had been so potent from that first day and which had lost none of its power. 'Georgia?' He was puzzled, concerned, tender even—all those fine emotions which were such a sham. She would have preferred to see anger, which would have given her the chance to strike back.

'Nat.' It was impossible to say if her smile held any conviction, but something in her tone caused his eyes to narrow.

'What. . .what is going on?' His fingers flicked to her bag, to the boarding card in her hand then back to her face. 'Have you had bad news of some kind?'

'No, nothing like that.' Georgia's smile felt like a grimace but she was possessed by an overwhelming urge; she wanted to hurt him as he had hurt her, but without revealing a clue about the depths of her own pain. Her words when she heard them were as much of a shock to her as they were to Nathan. 'I had a call from Jordan.

You remember I told you about him? and he has offered me my job back, so—' she shrugged '—I thought it was best to accept.'

'You. . .you *what*?' Nat shook his head, put one hand to his forehead, waited a moment for her to reply, and when she didn't he added, 'And what about us?' His voice was very low, hostile even.

'That was a mistake.' Again she had no idea what she was going to say till she opened her mouth. One part of her was inclined to scream accusations, but in the end pride held her back from making a scene. Perhaps if they had been alone together she would have been able to bring up the matter of the wife and child he had carelessly omitted to mention.

And pride came into it too, on a different level. How could she, a woman who knew the ways of the world, have made the same idiotic mistake again? To become involved with a married man twice in as many months! Her self-esteem was in tatters, and the only restorative was to try to eradicate the memory of it from her mind.

'A mistake?' His face might have lost colour but that was most likely to do with the artificial lighting in this place.

'I'm sorry, Nat.' Why? she asked herself. Why on earth was she apologising? 'Would you please stop holding me?' Her voice wobbled. 'You're hurting my arm.'

Without a word he released her, stood staring

down. The grey eyes which could sparkle so light-heartedly were icy and withdrawn, and Georgia found herself, in spite of everything, longing above all to put her head down on his chest, ask him to deny everything, to comfort her and to mend her heart, which she knew without doubt was broken in pieces.

'I'm waiting, Georgia.'

'I said, didn't I? It was a mistake. Simple as that.' With a feeling of desperation she raised her head as an announcement was made on the address system. 'I think that's my flight being called. I must go; I—'

'That is a flight for Baghdad, but I don't for a minute imagine you're heading in that direction. And, in any event, you're not going anywhere until you give me an explanation—and just to say it was a mistake isn't nearly enough.'

'Your friends are looking for you.' She gestured towards the group he had left. 'Why don't you go back and—?

'I'm waiting, Georgia. I'm trying to hang onto my temper but, if I do lose it, I won't have the least hesitation in bundling you into a car and seeing that you're kept in Raqat for just as long as it suits me.'

'I don't believe you. You—'

'The short man in that group is one of the chief ministers. All I have to do is invent one or two missing articles—the property of the Sheikh, you see—and you would be detained until the matter was cleared to their satisfaction.'

'You. . .you wouldn't do that. Not to me.'

'Why not? You're prepared to take some kind of cruel revenge on me.'

'No, I'm not. It's—' Accusations almost spilled from her mouth but she choked them back, struggling for control. 'It's as I said, Nat, and I don't want to hurt you.' And that was true, she realised numbly; even though he had behaved so abominably to her, there had been no pleasure in her attempt to wound him. 'It's simply. . . I made a mistake when I left my job, and. . .'

It would have been convincing if she had been able to add Jordan's name to imply a more personal reason for wishing to return but the words would, she knew, stick in her throat. 'I'm. . . I'm sorry.' Silently she cursed herself for being a fool; the last thing he deserved from her was an apology, but perhaps this was the most dignified way to sever their relationship.

'I see. In that case—' he gave a weary little shrug—one which tugged at her emotions '—I'm sorry too, Georgia.'

'I. . .' She could hardly bear to look at his face— there was so much pain and desolation. And, after all, who was she to judge? She didn't imagine for a minute that Marylou would be the kind of wife he. . .'Nat, I. . .'

But whatever she had been about to say was

interrupted by a loud and insistent announcement which was impossible to ignore. They stared at each other for a long, fraught moment, then she said, quite gently, 'You're being paged, Nat. It sounds pretty urgent.'

'What? Oh...oh, yes.' A young woman in the uniform of Raqat Airlines, clipboard in hand, came hurrying across and Nathan took a step in her direction, inclining his head to hear what she had to say.

And at the same time, Georgia heard her flight being announced and seized the opportunity to hurry through to the departure lounge without another backward glance. It wasn't until she was flying high over the Mediterranean that she appreciated how very close she had come to making excuses for him, which could very easily have led to her being persuaded to put off her journey, to talk things through, and even to say goodbye to him properly.

The very idea made her shiver. She lay back in her seat in utter exhaustion, and only then allowed a few easing tears to trickle down her cheeks.

CHAPTER NINE

FOUR weeks later, the events in Raqat seemed like a dream, as Georgia sat in a hire van threading its way through London's early-evening traffic, a mini collection of her clothes in the back, *en route* to a prestigious fashion show at a top hotel. Since it was a major charity affair there was no money in it, but, as her father had said when trying to rouse her interest, the publicity itself could be worth thousands.

'It's Connie Bering's pet charity, as I explained.' In the drawing room of his Greenwich home William Maitland had poured two sherries, holding one out to his daughter. 'When she rang the other day asking for your help I had to explain you were out of the country. Then—' he'd leaned against the mantelpiece, studying his younger daughter whose gaze was so firmly fixed on the garden '—when you came back so unexpectedly...' He'd paused to give her the chance to explain, had had no result, so had continued. 'It seemed to me like a good idea. You know David and I served together in Aden. Since he inherited the title, Connie's social conscience has gone wild! I won't tell you what a little flibbertigibbet she

150

was way back. That sherry all right for you, Georgy?'

'Hmm?' With a start she'd come back to the present, smiled extravagantly and sipped. 'You were saying about Lady B?'

'Just that. . .it might be worth your while helping with this fashion show, especially—' William had seemed to be choosing his words with care '—if you haven't anything lined up.'

'No.' At last she'd realised that something was expected of her. 'But I mean to start looking tomorrow.'

'Well, why not do this first? They're offering an allowance to buy materials, and proper machinists have been taken on. It might be fun, and I understand a TV company is doing a full-length feature, and lots of the big retail outlets are sending their reps. As I said, the publicity could be worth a great deal.'

And that was why, in the intervening weeks since the conversation, Georgia had found herself working harder than she ever had before, harder than she would have believed possible—so hard that the moment her head touched the pillow at night she was sound asleep. And if she did invariably wake in the early hours reaching out for Nat, his name on her lips, that was a temporary aberration, something she would deal with in time, since her determination to obliterate every last memory was fierce as ever.

Only. . .only, it wasn't easy. There was still this sense of betrayal and bitterness that he had made no attempt to contact her, to offer some kind of explanation or apology, however feeble.

Not that she wanted to retain contact; in fact that was the very last thing. . . But had he wanted to then it would have been comparatively simple for him to have approached Pete Taylor for her address.

But most likely he would have been too ashamed. She could just begin to imagine the kinds of stories that had been flying around Raqat after their breakup.

'Here we are, then.' Her driver manoeuvred the vehicle into the parking area and a moment later was helping her carry the carefully shrouded dresses in through the side-door, up a back staircase to the rooms set aside for the models to change. Thereafter, it was sheer chaos as everyone jostled for space to deal with last-minute jobs, and Georgia barely had time for her own preparations before being called to present her collection.

At least, knowing she herself looked good—she was wearing the wide, filmy trousers and the tunic-top that she had worn that first night with. . . Knowing she looked good gave her confidence, and she was happy with the designs she had put together.

She had decided to emphasise the fun side of

dressing, using a number of the sketches she had done when she was in...the Middle East. The outfits were mainly exotic and impractical, but then this audience was not interested in practicality; lavish luxury was the everyday lifestyle of most.

She had been lucky, too, in the girls who had been allocated to model her clothes. They were highly professional, stunningly attractive; even *she* gasped in admiration and mild disbelief at the fact that she had created something so gorgeous when the first model drifted dreamily across the upper balcony before beginning her slow descent. The girl was so tall and sinuous, with the kind of figure that men, and women too, would drool over, and her coffee-coloured skin did wondrous things to the cream-coloured chiffon.

Then all at once Georgia realised that the audience was waiting to hear from her, the designer, and she panicked, looked desperately in the direction that she expected to see her father. But with the lights dimmed it was impossible to pick him out. Hundreds of heads seemed to be turning expectantly towards where she stood on the half-landing; there was no escape, so she straightened her backbone, cleared her throat and began.

'Lara looks stunning in Desert Aubade.' Well, they certainly didn't need her to tell them *that*!

Barefoot, Lara glided to the bottom of the

thickly carpeted staircase and turned to where a
discreet fan blew the delicate material against her
body, giving a momentary impression of her form
beneath the chiffon, before she moved on and the
dress floated away from her; she paused dramati-
cally, swirled about her shoulders the scarf which
had been trailing from her fingers, and disappeared as the next girl appeared at the top of the
staircase.

The ripple of applause gave Georgia confidence
and, being so familiar with the clothes, she felt
she could dispense with the flash cards she had
prepared and found herself talking easily, casually
as the dresses came and went.

A tiny hiatus gave her a moment to search
again for her father, and just as she thought she
might have found him a door to one side opened
quite suddenly, spilling a beam of light, illuminat-
ing a tall male figure lounging against a wall.
There was something so achingly familiar about it
that she drew in a sharp, painful breath, but the
door closed almost as soon as it had opened
and. . .she knew she had been mistaken.

Her mind played funny tricks. She had lost
count of the times when she had firmly identified
him then a moment later had found there wasn't
the slightest resemblance, but. . .but now Mhairi
was waiting, and heavens, she had forgotten what
she was modelling. Where was her card?

Then it was her last outfit, once again being

enhanced by Lara's inimitable style. 'We bring to an end the first half of the show with Lara wearing Masquerade which she does with her usual panache.'

This time the girl moved with tiny, dancing steps which caused the harem trousers to billow, the bells about her ankles to jingle lightly. The see-through green silk gave tantalising glimpses of skin, the matching briefs preserved a little modesty, though discretion was not the name of this game! A loose cropped top just covered her bosom, but was weighted down with tiny silver coins which offered some covering. In her navel was a brilliant—and how difficult it had been to persuade it to adhere. Her face was hidden behind a gilt mask which she held on a stick and behind which her eyes glittered with wicked amusement before she danced out of sight.

From Georgia's point of view the evening had been a great success, and she responded to the enthusiastic applause by raising both hands in appreciation. As the lights came on her eyes were drawn to the rear of the room, but of course she saw no one. And even if the figure had still lounged negligently there it would have been that of a total stranger.

Some time upstairs dealing with the aftermath, a hurried word with her father, and she was free to watch the rest of the show from the hidden vantage point reserved for helpers. A tartan theme was exciting her interest when a page touched her arm enquiringly. 'Miss Georgia Maitland?' And when she nodded he handed her an envelope.

A single sheet of the hotel notepaper requested that she go to Suite 309 as soon as possible. Puzzled, she shrugged, and was about to throw it aside when an older woman, one of the committee members, reminded her that several of the large retail houses had sent out their scouts in search of new talents.

'I'm not so sure.' Georgia frowned indecisively.

'But what have you to lose? You'd be a fool to miss a chance and I know your designs were particularly admired. You ought to give it a go.'

'I suppose so.' It was, after all, one of the reasons she was here—the hope of giving her moribund career a boost. But she was feeling weary, in no mood to make career decisions. And—why not admit it?—she was upset by that fancied glimpse. . .

'You might regret it.'

'All right.' She smiled at the woman. 'I'm going, I'm going. And if anyone wants me you'll know where I can be found.'

When Georgia reached the third floor she found the door to Suite 309 open, but when she walked inside there were none of the signs that she would have expected—no trays of coffee or drinks, nothing to indicate an executive from a

major outlet, his briefcase bulging with induce-
ments. . . Only, behind a sofa she could see a
small table set with two places and. . .she thought
it was time to go. She turned towards the door.

'Georgia.'

She froze then, heard her pulses beating loudly
in her ears before she could find the strength to
turn round. The voice, the way he spoke her name
were so difficult to resist. The look of him too,
formally dressed for the city—dark suit, pink-
striped shirt and. . . Pain caught at her heart. How
dared he wear a cream rosebud in his buttonhole?
He needn't imagine that any such tactics would
have any effect.

But he was thinner—just a little. There were
signs of strain about the eyes, a few lines round
the mouth that she didn't remember, but then, his
wife would most likely have given him a hard
time. A lump in her throat refused to clear.

'Nathan.' She spoke his name after a pause that
seemed endless, while each gazed at the other,
and then, in an attempt to be casual, she said, 'I
did think I caught a glimpse of you downstairs
but then. . .' She gnawed at her lower lip.

'I loved your clothes.' He gave a faint smile.
'So. . .perhaps some good came from Raqat.'

'I doubt it. I thought. . .' Her voice broke and
she paused, struggling for control. 'I thought. . .'
That was better—her voice was much stronger

and assured and. . .detached. 'I really thought I was being invited to meet a possible client.'

'I'm sorry. I didn't want to risk you baling out again before I had the chance. . . And when your father said—'

'My father!' She was instantly inflamed at the possibility of collusion. 'What has Dad to do with this?'

'Don't blame him, Georgia. I particularly asked him not to let you know I was here. I managed to trace his address and when I rang this morning he told me about the fashion show, where it was being held, and it seemed the obvious thing to book in here for my visit.'

'I see.' Determined to stay cool, she knew she would have something to say to her father when she saw him. How dared he interfere? 'But. . .' There was a knock on the door which Nathan acknowledged, and two waiters came into the room, bustling about with bottles and several covered silver dishes, which she supposed were the means by which he meant to get round her. If so, then he was much mistaken, even though she was hungry. 'I hope all this. . .' a wave of her hand indicated dismissive contempt '. . .is not on my account, for if it is then it will be entirely wasted.'

'Don't decide straight away, Georgia.' His tone was mild, he was unthreatening, and it crossed her mind as she watched him pour out drinks, return with glasses clinking with ice, that she remembered having had that same opinion before, and look where that had got her.

'Gin and tonic.' His eyes were smiling at her now; she ached to respond but would not allow it. 'Remember? And it couldn't be weaker.'

'Thank you.' It would be ridiculous to refuse, to rush down the corridor like Red Riding Hood escaping from the wolf—ridiculous but not entirely inappropriate, she decided on a wave of unexpected amusement. Besides, she was tired and deserved a drink to revive her after such a frantic day.

'Sit down, Georgia.' And she did, quite obediently but watching suspiciously, not entirely at the mercy of the quick rush of alcohol in her veins. 'You've led me quite a dance—do you know that?'

'Really?' She had meant the single word to drip sarcasm, but instead it came out more as a polite query.

'I knew nothing about your father's address except that he was in the London area. If it hadn't been for his army rank, my search might have taken me much longer.'

Really! Did he think she was so naïve? 'I would have thought, if you were so anxious to trace me—' she picked up her glass and took a mouthful of gin and tonic, '—you could have asked Pete Taylor. He could have provided the necessary information.'

'Ah, yes, Pete.' Nat seemed to consider. 'I did think of it, believe me, but with him in Raqat and me. . .'

'I suppose you felt some shame.'

'Look, Georgia—' it pleased her that she had at least got under his skin, that he was showing some reaction '—let's stop fencing, shall we? I haven't flown thousands of miles so we can dance about exchanging cryptic comments. I've no idea what you mean by that last remark but you told me, didn't you, that you were coming back to your old job with your previous employer? But according to your father—'

'Dad had no right.' Her glass hit the side-table with a crash. 'I resent the idea of you two discussing me behind my back.'

'You shouldn't, you know.' His voice was calm but the air of sorrow was like a blow to her heart.

'Wh-what do you mean?'

'You ought not to resent us talking of you. He loves you. . .while I. . .' He shrugged with a hopeless resignation.

Yes, Georgia knew her father loved her, but Nathan? At one time she had believed that he too. . .

'Will you listen to me, Georgia? Just for a few moments, I promise you. I've been so desperate about what went wrong.'

'Oh, I believe you.' Now she could no longer control her own anguish. 'So desperate it took you weeks and weeks—' Her voice broke, and when Nat took a step closer she did not move away.

'You think that was my choice?'

She shrugged, raked a distracted hand through her hair, raised tear-drenched eyes. 'What am I supposed to think?'

'Georgia?' That voice, once so irresistible, had lost none of its power. 'Georgia.' He spoke her name on a sigh, then, reaching out, put his hands on her shoulders, giving her a gentle shake. 'You think it hasn't been hell for me?'

She experienced a momentary surge of joy before she remembered—she must not allow him to beguile. 'Does it matter?'

'To me it does. More than anything else in the world. Listen to me, Georgia.' And when she would have interrupted he said fiercely, 'Listen! That day at the airport when you were about to board I was being paged—do you remember that?' He saw one reluctant move of her head. 'Well, it was a frantic message from my mother. My father had been in a major automobile pile-up and was badly hurt. If it hadn't been for that, I promise you, I'd have been on the next plane for Heathrow.'

It was ridiculous to find some consolation in that, but at least it was a partial salve for her bitterness; besides, she knew how attached to his parents he was. 'I'm sorry, I had no idea. How. . . how is your father?'

'He was in a coma for several days, then he confounded everyone by waking up and starting to talk about the details of a contract he had been working on just before the accident. He has a broken arm and some spinal damage, but the doctors are now convinced he'll make a complete recovery.

'In the meantime, I've had to give a great deal of time to the New York office, as there were several important deals in the offing. That and nothing else would have kept me away for so long but. . . Don't forget, it was *you* who decided that it had all been a mistake, that you were coming back to that man. Can you imagine how I felt, the blow to my pride? Here I was, having brought the discussions in Cairo to an end ahead of time, just so I could get back to you, and I found myself tossed aside. . . I thought we had something unique going—something that would last us for the rest of our lives and. . .'

She must stop this before things got out of hand, before she allowed him to persuade her to do what she knew was wrong and which was bound to end in misery for both of them. And yet, it would be so easy. Even now she longed to reach out, to caress his cheek with the back of her hand, knowing—oh they had become so expert in pleasing each other—that he would catch her fingers, drop kisses against the tender skin of her palm. How delicious and dangerous it had all seemed, how utterly right. And yet all the time he had been deceiving her, and not only her but his. . .

Georgia drew in a deep breath and took a step backwards to be further from his influence.

'And what about your wife, Nathan?' She surprised herself with her calm, steadfast determination. 'Where did she come into this equation of unique and lifelong devotion?'

'My. . .?' Her words had shocked him. She could see the sudden change in his expression— the darkening of his eyes from the silvery to cold steel-grey, the tightening of the well-shaped mouth.

'Mmm.' If only she were feeling as uninvolved as she sounded. If only she were reflecting on the sorrow of a friend rather than on this tearing unhappiness deep inside. 'It's amazing how many men have this attitude towards their wives. Out of sight, out of—'

'Who have you been talking to?' Then, when she didn't immediately answer, Nat gave a scoffing, weary laugh. 'As if I need to ask. I suppose Melanie Jacobs was only too pleased—'

'I don't think I set eyes on Melanie except when I was with you. No. . .' Now she almost felt as if she was going to enjoy herself. He had caused her so much anguish. Now it was *his* turn, and she savoured each word.

'No, it was your *wife* who came to the flat one day—The very day we met at the airport, in fact. She was very surprised to see me there and I decided to do the decent thing and made myself scarce. I'm surprised you didn't know all about our meeting.' Remembering the humiliation of it brought colour to her cheeks. 'Or perhaps—' there was a hiss in her voice which she could not control '—perhaps it is such an everyday occurrence that it wasn't worth mentioning.'

'I knew nothing about it.' His face was pale; it needed no special insight to see that he was ablaze with anger. 'I didn't go back to the apartment after that emergency call. I left for New York less than an hour after you took off, and when I saw Marylou in the States ten days ago she made no mention of having been in Raqat. But then she wouldn't,' he concluded with considerable bitterness.

Although she had expected nothing from their meeting—nothing except an unloading of some of her bitterness—Georgia experienced a great sense of anticlimax. Even now there had been the faint hope that some fairy might wave a wand and make things come right, but she was much too old to believe in fairy tales. . .should have known better.

'Can you forgive me, Georgia?' Of course she

could. All her bitterness had evaporated; she just hoped that if he tried to persuade her she would have the strength to resist. 'I've treated you badly and I wouldn't blame you if. . .'

His finger came out, took a strand of her hair and twisted it round—a gesture that she had always found inexplicably erotic, and which now sent a shiver racking down her spine. But he didn't follow it up as he always had. He didn't pull her gently into the curve of his body, slide his hand the length of her spine and drive her out of her mind with the touch of his mouth.

'Perhaps it's Marylou whose forgiveness ought to be on your mind?' She dared not allow her emotional response to obscure the fact of his marriage and his. . . 'And your daughter's.' The very idea of him having a child with a woman who wasn't Georgia Maitland was like a knife in her breast. 'Not mine.' A sob burst out before she could control it, then another. 'Not a silly, impressionable woman who allowed her head to be turned by all the romantic flim-flam of the desert.'

Now she was sobbing in earnest, hadn't the strength to resist when Nat put his arms about her and pulled her close.

'Don't cry, my darling; you're breaking my heart.'

'I'm not crying,' Georgia spluttered, and there

was the tiniest surge of amusement when he laughed softly.

'You could have fooled me.' But he let her go when she pulled away, took an immaculately laundered handkerchief from his pocket and held it out to her. 'And now I'm going to do what I ought to have done right back at the beginning.' His face was grim, like his voice. 'I'm going to tell you about Marylou. And about Philippa.'

And when he said those names any last flicker of hope she might have been nurturing just gave up and died.

CHAPTER TEN

'ARE you hungry, Georgia?'

Outrage and resentment at such a question only increased when she suddenly realised she *was* hungry—more than that, she was ravenous. 'What sort of question is that?' The chill in her voice was touched with disdain.

'An inappropriate one,' Nat confessed with a humility of which she was instantly suspicious—it went so oddly with his characteristic aura of easy self-assurance. 'But since I ordered what I hope will be a delicious meal, and since I've hardly eaten all day, and as there is a bottle of rather nice red. . . But, of course, if you aren't hungry, it hardly matters.' The raised eyebrow and faint smile were disconcerting enough to make her feel apologetic.

'Well, as it happens, I am a *bit* hungry.'

'Then sit here.' A chair was held out. He checked that she was comfortably settled before he removed the silver domes from the dishes, took the seat opposite and with a sigh—weariness or content: it was impossible for her to decide which—poured the wine.

For a long moment he sat watching her with

that cool, clear look which had such instant appeal. 'Are you going to drink, Georgia?' And he raised his glass encouragingly, the silvery-grey eyes taking in the veil of hair which had drifted over her forehead, lingering on her mouth in a way that made her tremble.

She had forgotten—or perhaps she had just blotted them from her mind—so many things. Such long sooty lashes, for one. Sometimes when they had been very close she had felt them brush against her cheek—a strange and quite wonderful sensation. The many tiny habits and gestures, for another. In a moment Nat would push back the hair from his forehead and. . .

He was watching her intently, a little half-smile on his face, as if he could read her mind, could judge that already she was mellowing. But then— she forced herself to be brisk—he had had, if his wife was to be believed, much practice in situations exactly like this.

Pain racked her again; she stifled the urge to cry out, reached instead for her glass, which of course brought him back to his previous point.

'To us?' His voice had always exerted such a profound effect.

'Is there. . .?' Georgia began, and then stopped, put down the glass and reached for the fork, looking down instead at the medallions of lamb, tiny sprays of green mangetout, baby carrots, herbed new potatoes—colourful as a still life. She

broke off a sliver of meat and ate a tiny mouthful,
'Mmm, delicious. Why don't you begin?' She had
intended to be irritating but had had no success if
his expression of amused tolerance was anything
to go by.

'To us?' Nat suggested again, glass still raised
in her direction.

'Is there—' she continued with the put-down
she had begun earlier '—any reason why we
should?'

'I very much hope there is.'

Georgia raised her glass to her mouth, drank,
and replaced it on the table, giving her attention
once more to the food. 'You seem to imagine that
whatever you want will come about. You ride
roughshod over everyone's inclinations and
emotions. . .' Her voice broke. She put down her
fork.

'I didn't know I had done that.' His voice was
sober now, sorrowful, and without looking she
knew that he hadn't even started to eat. 'I thought
what happened between us in Raqat was what we
both wanted. It was only later you gave me reason
to think. . . I had been a substitute.'

'No.' The denial burst from her lips, instant and
passionate. 'Never, never that; you. . .' Remembering her uninhibited response to his lovemaking, she appealed, 'You cannot believe that.'

'So—' the silver of his expressive eyes gleamed

as if it had caught the light '—the scene at the airport. . .?'

'Was sheer self-defence; surely that was obvious?' She allowed her anger to take over; it was easier to feel angry than to soften and. . . 'Your wife appears on the scene, questions me about my role in your life; what else could I do but salve my pride? I wasn't going to break down at the airport and let the whole world know what a fool I'd been. It was enough to know myself, to realise how I had been taken in by that ridiculous charade in the desert. . .'

Her voice broke and the green eyes brimmed with tears she refused to let fall, while she stared with accusation.

'That, Georgia, wasn't a charade. I told you at the time—there was a reason.'

'Yes, but you would, wouldn't you? You didn't ever explain what the reason was.'

'Permission for you to remain in Raqat was the reason. They're pretty hot on visitors who over-stay, and when I spoke about it to Freddy the marriage ceremony was his solution. I think you'll agree it was romantic, but I knew perfectly well you would want to have the position regularised when we came back to the UK. That was what I planned—'

'Except, of course—' now she could not disguise her feelings of triumph '—you had forgotten one very important drawback.' Green eyes flashed a challenge that she knew he could not meet, yet he returned her gaze steadily for a longish moment before replying.

'If you're referring to Marylou, then no, I hadn't forgotten.'

'You. . .' It was impossible to think of any comeback, and triumph could be such a very unsatisfactory emotion. What she longed for was proof that *she* was in the wrong; how she would have welcomed the opportunity to. . .

'Don't say any more, Georgia.' Nat's hand came out to cover hers. 'Let me tell you about Marylou.'

'About your *wife*,' she insisted, driving a knife still more deeply into her heart. 'Let's not avoid the relationship.'

'Marylou has never been my real wife.'

At first she didn't understand what he had said. She was too involved with the immediate problem of stopping her tears to allow the words to penetrate, but then the room seemed to be spinning about her. She reached out a hand to save her wineglass. 'What?' A frown drew her eyebrows together. 'What did you say?'

'Twelve years ago I married Marylou; it was in name only. . .'

'Oh, yes?' Did he imagine that she was so gullible? Did he have any idea what sort of roller coaster he was putting her on with his explanations? 'What about the tiny detail of Philippa?'

'To put it at its simplest, my relationship with Philippa is that of uncle, but I'm not sure even about that.'

Abruptly Georgia removed her hand from his. Direct contact with them had always, she felt, worked to her disadvantage, had made it more difficult for her to be coolly rational. She said nothing, stared, trying to come to terms with, even to understand what he had said.

There was candour in the grey eyes returning her gaze; surely that wasn't assumed? With all her heart and soul she wanted to believe, but there had been so much bad faith and she had been so badly hurt. 'Why?' It was a cry of despair. 'Why should I believe you now?'

That got to him. It was clear in the suddenly altered expression, the painful grimace, the inward struggle before he could control himself. 'Because it's true. I can think of no better reason. Not that I blame you for doubting me. I blame myself for not telling you right back at the beginning. I simply kept putting it off, waiting for the right moment. For one thing, I never thought of myself as a married man, and secondly our relationship was so special. Maybe I didn't want anything to diminish it.'

'Your *niece*?' The story was one she could scarcely unravel. 'You say Philippa is your *niece*?'

'You remember once I told you I had a brother, younger than I, killed in a skiing accident in

Colorado? Well, shortly afterwards Marylou—Phil had brought her home once or twice—well, she appeared saying that they had intended to marry and she was expecting his child. My mother was still traumatised because of the accident, and she got the idea that Phil's son would be his reincarnation. He had to have the family name so he could, in due course, fulfil his father's role. It must sound like the craziest kind of blackmail, but the only thing that would comfort her was the thought of my marrying Marylou so the line could be unbroken. In the end I agreed. We had one of those five-minute ceremonies in front of a Justice, and immediately I knew I had made a ghastly mistake. As soon as I could, I got a Reno divorce and put the matter to the back of my mind.

'When Philippa was born it was a bit of an anti-climax for Mother, who had been so sure it would be a boy, and in the meantime Marylou became a cross we had to bear. As I implied, I'm by no means convinced Philippa is a Trehearn. Marylou and Philip both led pretty rackety lives at that stage and I have this idea she was simply securing the best possible future for herself and the child.

'That she has done, most successfully, but from my point of view she has been more of a pain—turning up out of the blue, trying to persuade me that Philippa is longing to see me, for us all to be a family again.' He gave a sudden grimace. 'Exactly what we never were.'

'And you think she isn't? Longing to see you again, I mean.'

'I'm sure she isn't. For one thing, even if she were, I doubt Marylou would be aware of it. Philippa is at a very good boarding-school near Boston. I know she's happy there and I don't think she misses family life as much as Marylou pretends. She has turned into a pleasant, well-balanced girl in spite of everything.'

'But you're not certain that she's even your niece?'

'I can't decide. There's no physical resemblance. She's more like her mother than any of us, but occasionally there's an expression, a turn of the head... On the other hand when I suggested to Marylou that we have some tests done she changed the subject abruptly and took to her heels.'

'So...'

'So maybe she herself isn't one hundred per cent certain.' His shrug was weary. 'That's the whole not very elevating tale, Georgia. I'll always regret waiting so long to—'

'Nathan.' Still it was difficult for her to understand what had happened. This feeling of euphoria was too good to be true; she didn't entirely trust anything that had raised her from such Stygian gloom so abruptly. And as for the altered reality of her own position—well, on that she had better reserve judgement. For the moment it was enough to know that Nat, the man she would adore for the rest of her life, was not, had never been involved with Marylou. He was not Philippa's father, perhaps not even her uncle, and. . .

'Yes?' A touch on her hand brought her from her reverie, then, when she turned a brilliant, glowing look on him, he smiled with a touch of apology. 'You spoke my name. It was as if you were about to ask a question.'

'Oh.' It was ridiculous to blush, to feel shy as she was doing, to look down at the table. Then, with an upward glance immediately hidden by long dark lashes, she said, 'I suppose that was all I wanted to say just then. Nathan. Nothing else.'

There was no resistance when he took her hand to his mouth and kissed the open palm, all without taking his eyes from her face. Then he said, 'I thought you would have trusted me.'

Eyes flew open, blazed greenly at him. 'I'm sorry.' Georgia spoke so passionately that it was impossible to doubt her. No words existed to express the depths of her sorrow; even to herself she could not now explain why she had chosen to believe Marylou, except. . .except her act had carried such conviction. 'You see, Marylou came into the apartment as if she knew it. She was so entirely at home. . .'

'She was there just once before. Melanie is her friend—the *family* friend,' he added drily. 'I'm pretty sure Melanie must have told her about us, and she flew over to try to spoil things. But I know if anyone had concocted such lies about you I would at least have asked for your side of the story.'

'Nathan—' her face twisted in distress '—what more can I say? I'm penitent beyond description. I'll wear sackcloth and ashes. . .'

'That'll be the day.' He was grinning. Her heart lifted in wild response, lips curved. . .

'And I'll do anything to atone.'

'I *might* be able to devise a suitable forfeit.' Her heart was hammering against her ribs; she could feel the surge of blood in her veins. 'But I shall want an immediate answer to what I have in mind.'

'Yes?' Georgia tried not to sound too eager, too anxious to fall in with whatever plan Nat devised. But she knew that if he swept her up and carried her into the bedroom she was ready to be coerced, seduced, or whatever he had in mind. More than ready—impatient. So when he spoke his words were very nearly an anticlimax.

'What are you doing tomorrow afternoon?'

'Tomorrow afternoon?' Her mind went blank. What was wrong with this moment?

'I've arranged for a special licence and that is the very earliest time. . . But if you must put on a show I can wait a few days. No charade this time, but a simple ceremony—one which might set lots of tongues wagging but which we shall know means only one thing—that I cannot exist any longer without you. . .'

'Oh, Nathan.' Unexpectedly her eyes filled with tears, though why that should be the case when she was so blissfully, so lyrically happy she didn't know. She raised a hand, touched his face with the air of a collector who had made a unique find. 'We cannot exist any longer without each other.'

He caught her hand, held it still for a few moments. 'I shouldn't do that, because. . . I did tell your father I would let him know your answer.' Georgia's expression brought a snort of amusement from him. 'And I do not want him to come up here and find his innocent daughter in bed with a man. Besides, you still haven't given me a direct answer to my question. Don't keep me in suspense any longer.'

'Yes. Yes. *Yes.*' She whirled away from him, arms wrapped about herself in an excess of joy then when he caught her they collapsed onto the sofa together.

'I love you.' He pushed her back into the cushions as he loomed over her, his face serious. 'I love you to distraction, and when I thought I had lost you. . .when I imagined you with another man. . .'

'Then maybe you can imagine how I felt when I thought that you were married to Marylou, that you had a daughter with her.'

'I can't imagine why you didn't trust me. . .'

'For the rest of our lives I shall have complete faith. You will be the most trusted man in the world.'

'Don't make any promises you might find difficult to keep!'

'I shall find it easy.' Smilingly she linked her hands at the back of his neck, inclining his mouth towards her. 'So long as you keep doing. . .this. . . and. . .this.' She interspersed her words with kisses.

'The thing is—' Nat spoke softly against her cheek '—if we keep on doing this—and this, then I doubt if we'll get down to see your father, and since we have that rather important date tomorrow afternoon it might be better to put him in the picture.

'And something else. . .' With great determination he detached himself from her clinging arms, stood, looking down in self-mocking frustration while straightening his tie and raking fingers through his hair in that familiar gesture. 'I did promise that if I could put everything right with you I wouldn't rush things, no matter what the temptation. I said I would wait till the ring had been properly placed on your finger. That was the commitment I made—one I don't intend to break, no matter how much you provoke me. So. . .don't make life difficult for both of us, Georgia. I promise you, after tomorrow my vow of celibacy ends and you can be as seductive as you like. I shall guarantee maximum response. But now—' reaching for her hand, he pulled her gently to her feet and into his arms '—let's go down and speak with your father. But, just so there's no possible chance of misunderstanding, I love you. Beginning of story.'

CHAPTER ELEVEN

'REMEMBER,' Georgia sighed, leaning her head against Nat's shoulder, 'you promised me a glimpse of paradise. But this—' his arm tightening about her waist caused a tiny shiver '—this is sheer heaven.'

From the garden of the villa the view of sea, burnished and gleaming as the sun dropped into it, was breathtaking, and they stood for a few moments simply watching as the fiery disc disappeared, leaving a hundred shades of cinnabar and gold in its wake.

'Mmm,' he agreed, dropping a swift kiss on her head. 'A shock when you were so sure you were going to wake up in Raqat.'

'Well, since I knew nothing of the existence of your family villa in the Caribbean, it didn't really enter into my calculations.'

'Disappointed?'

She swung round, her expression halfway between a smile and a pout, as she took his face between her palms and shook her head with slow emphasis. 'I would not be disappointed if we were to spend our honeymoon in Siberia, but—'

'But you do prefer this? You're making me

anxious with those longing references to Siberia.'
And they laughed, kissed and laughed again.

'I'm so sorry I was dead on my feet when we
arrived.' Blushing a little, she laid her head
against his heart.

It was disconcerting to think that after all the
anxiety, the impatience, the indecent haste of
their wedding which, when all was said and done,
had had one immediate aim, she had wrecked
their plans—had to be carried off the boat which
had brought them from the mainland, had only
once half wakened to murmur thanks to the maid
who had eased her out of her travel clothes, and
had then curled up on a cover to sleep off the
effects of the last two hectic days.

'I was afraid you might have picked up some
tummy bug.' Her look of reproach brought a grin.
'Which could have been very inhibiting on a honeymoon. So realising it was simple exhaustion. . . To
tell the truth I was pretty whacked myself, and
wasn't averse to catching up on some lost sleep.'

'Losing interest in your wife the moment you're
married?'

'I have quite recovered now. And that is a
promise. Oh—' Nat's attention was attracted by
something over her shoulder and Georgia turned
to see a servant on the terrace '—looks like dinner
is ready. Are you hungry?'

'Starving.' And they both laughed.

* * *

They ate on the terrace—chilled soup, broiled lobster, the most delicious fruit salad that Georgia had ever tasted—and drank a light champagne which heightened their sparkling excitement.

'I did tell you, didn't I?' They were drinking strong black coffee and he spoke casually. 'Another ordeal awaits when we reach the States.'

'Oh?' She felt a tiny frisson of anxiety. 'Meeting your parents—you think that will be an ordeal? I hope they'll—'

'Of course they will. They'll adore you almost as much as I do. My mother is particularly delighted. She's always been worried that my apparently endlessly unmarried state was due to the Marylou episode. It wasn't, of course. I was just waiting for you. But you're going to take a great load of guilt from her shoulders. No, I know you won't find meeting them an ordeal. What I did mean... Mother is even now organising an outsize wedding reception, to make up for the one she thinks we missed in London.'

'I see.'

'You don't mind?'

'Tonight I don't mind anything.'

'And, as a surprise, I've asked your parents and sister to come over.'

'Nathan! How wonderful.'

'And they've all promised to be there.'

'Oh. . .' She was smiling. 'But why should you think anything like that should be an ordeal?'

'I just wondered—thought it might be a charade too far for you.'

'I'm sorry to disappoint you but I'm quite prepared to marry you as often as you like.'

'Ah.' The grey eyes gleamed in appreciation and amusement. 'My sentiments exactly.' He leaned across and, taking her hand, touched the gold band placed there so recently. 'Has it occurred to you that this looks rather lonely?'

'No. I'm just so happy, and relieved to see it there.'

'So you don't yearn for a gorgeous jewel to match your eyes?'

'I didn't say that.'

'Just as well, since I bought this for you.'

Georgia looked at the little leather box, eyes widening as Nat pressed the stud and the lid flew back. 'It is just so lovely.' She held her breath as he slid the ring onto her finger, appraised it for a moment then nodded his agreement.

'It is, and I'm very glad. I wondered if maybe you'd prefer sapphires, or just diamonds, but this was so much the colour of your eyes. . .'

'You exaggerate so wildly.' But it was impossible to hide her delight. 'Thank you, my darling. You are—as I told you once before—spoiling me.'

'That is what I mean to do then,' he said huskily, 'and look what a mess I made of it.'

'When on earth did you find time to buy this,

Nathan?' She held out her hand, moving it so that the lights flashed on the emerald, sparkled on the surrounding diamonds. 'I would have thought you would have had far too much to do when you were in London to spare time to go round the jewellers...'

'I didn't buy it in London.'

'No?' She looked at him in surprise. 'Then where?'

'Believe it or not, I bought it in Cairo. I had it in my pocket that day at the airport.'

'Oh, Nathan.' Her face twisted with remorse. 'I'm so, so—'

'Shh.' His finger came across and touched her mouth. 'No more apologies. What happened was anguish while it lasted but maybe it will make us appreciate each other all the more. Certainly, right at this moment, *I* have no regrets.'

'Well...' She considered. 'I suppose if things hadn't happened as they did we might not be here right now, and I can't imagine anywhere on earth I would rather be. Not even the salt mines of Siberia,' she finished defiantly.

'Talking of travel to exotic places, you do know we'll have to go back to Raqat for a month or so? There are loose ends I must tie up, and after that I've little choice but to start pulling my weight in the business. Dad will be needing all the help he can get, so...'

'Will you miss it—the academic life, the freedom to take on exciting projects like the one in Raqat?'

'I don't imagine I'm going to miss anything—not with you beside me. I've been lucky to be able to do so many of the things I've enjoyed. I've had so much in life but the past few weeks have taught me one thing—the most important part of life is love. Take away the money, the success, all the trappings of the good life—all that matters in the end is love.' He rose, stretched, grinned at her and held out his hand. 'And, speaking of that. . .'

Arms about each other, they stood for a last look at the dark glitter of the ocean, then turned and wandered through the quiet house and into the large bedroom.

'Did I tell you—' Nat's voice was low, intimate as he wound a strand of her hair about his finger '—how beautiful you looked when you walked in with your father?'

'You did say. But I shan't be bored to hear it all again.'

'I loved that simple cotton dress and—'

'Simple,' she exploded in mock indignation, 'because I had no time! What other woman you know has had to arrange everything in about twelve hours?'

'And I loved the way you twisted your hair up into that topknot arrangement, with the spray of cream roses at the back, but—'

'Just as well I have a sister who knows about

these things. *And* a brother-in-law prepared to act as best man.'

'But on the whole I prefer your hair like this— long and silky, smelling of flowers when I bury my face in it.'

'And I thought you loved it when I wore a plait.'

'Ah. . .that.' He laughed. 'I'll tell you more about my reaction to that another time. I shan't embarrass you tonight of all nights.'

They stood smiling at each other in the foolish way so typical of their situation and Georgia could feel her pulses begin to quicken.

'I particularly like you in the dress you're wearing now.' To illustrate his point, his hand moved in a slow caress the length of her back; at the same time he inclined her into closer contact. 'And I wondered if there was any special reason for you choosing it?'

Delicately she reached up and placed her mouth against his. 'I didn't think that you would need reminding of this particular dress. I thought that you would know the reason.'

'I remember every single thing about that night.' Nat's hands brushed gently against her bare shoulders without disturbing the narrow shoestring straps.

'I do too. Why else do you think I brought it with me?' Georgia's voice was very low, her breathing shallow. 'Why else should I be wearing it tonight except to remind us?'

'As if I could ever forget. You came into the kitchen looking like the most delectable water sprite, dressed in the kind of scrap of a dress designed to drive men out of their minds. And you actually offered to make the meal, do you remember?'

'I told you,' she smiled dreamily. 'Everything I remember—every last detail.'

His laugh was soft but somehow thrilling. 'I meant to have you then. . .'

'But I trusted you,' she teased. 'I thought I was perfectly safe, and—'

'Until that moment I had imagined I could keep my feelings under control.'

'I knew I should never have left the security of Pete Taylor's flat.'

'If you had worn that dress downstairs, I might have been forced to come and rescue you. But I do admit—or, at least, if I were being interrogated by the Inquisition, I should swear to it—I had great difficulty in persuading you. . .'

'I promise that tonight you shall have no difficulty at all.'

'You remember that zipper caused me a great deal of frustration?'

'And you've forgotten where it is?'

'No, I've been thinking about it for the last five weeks!' And to confirm his total recall Nathan reached out for the tab and slowly pulled it down. . .

MILLS & BOON

Back by Popular Demand

BETTY NEELS

A collector's edition of favourite titles from one of the world's best-loved romance authors.

Mills & Boon are proud to bring back these sought after titles, now reissued in beautifully matching volumes and presented as one cherished collection.

Don't miss these unforgettable titles, coming next month:

Title #15 ROSES FOR CHRISTMAS
Title #16 CASSANDRA BY CHANCE

Available wherever
Mills & Boon books are sold

MILLS & BOON

Next Month's Romances

♡

Each month you can choose from a wide variety of romance with Mills & Boon. Below are the new titles to look out for next month in our two new series Presents and Enchanted.

Presents™

THEIR WEDDING DAY	Emma Darcy
THE FINAL PROPOSAL	Robyn Donald
HIS BABY!	Sharon Kendrick
MARRIED FOR REAL	Lindsay Armstrong
MISTLETOE MAN	Kathleen O'Brien
BAD INFLUENCE	Susanne McCarthy
TORN BY DESIRE	Natalie Fox
POWERFUL PERSUASION	Margaret Mayo

Enchanted™

THE VICAR'S DAUGHTER	Betty Neels
BECAUSE OF THE BABY	Debbie Macomber
UNEXPECTED ENGAGEMENT	Jessica Steele
BORROWED WIFE	Patricia Wilson
ANGEL BRIDE	Barbara McMahon
A WIFE FOR CHRISTMAS	Pamela Bauer & Judy Kaye
ALL SHE WANTS FOR CHRISTMAS	Liz Fielding
TROUBLE IN PARADISE	Grace Green

SINGLE LETTER SWITCH

A year's supply of Mills & Boon Presents™ novels— absolutely FREE!

Would you like to win a year's supply of passionate compelling and provocative romances? Well, you can and the're free! Simply complete the grid below and send it to us by 31st May 1997. The first five correct entries picked after the closing date will win a year's supply of Mills & Boon Presents™ novels (six books every month—worth over £150). What could be easier?

S	T	O	C	K
P	L	A	T	E

Clues:

A   To pile up
B   To ease off or a reduction
C   A dark colour
D   Empty or missing
E   A piece of wood
F   Common abbreviation for an aircraft

Please turn over for details of how to enter ☞

How to enter...

There are two five letter words provided in the grid overleaf. The first one being STOCK the other PLATE. All you have to do is write down the words that are missing by changing just one letter at a time to form a new word and eventually change the word STOCK into PLATE. You only have eight chances but we have supplied you with clues as to what each one is. Good Luck!

When you have completed the grid don't forget to fill in your name and address in the space provided below and pop this page into an envelope (you don't even need a stamp) and post it today. Hurry—competition ends 31st May 1997.

Mills & Boon® Single Letter Switch
FREEPOST
Croydon
Surrey
CR9 3WZ

Are you a Reader Service Subscriber?   Yes ❑   No ❑

Ms/Mrs/Miss/Mr _____

Address _____

_____

_____ Postcode _____

One application per household.

You may be mailed with other offers from other reputable companies as a result of this application. If you would prefer not to receive such offers, please tick box.   ❑

C6K